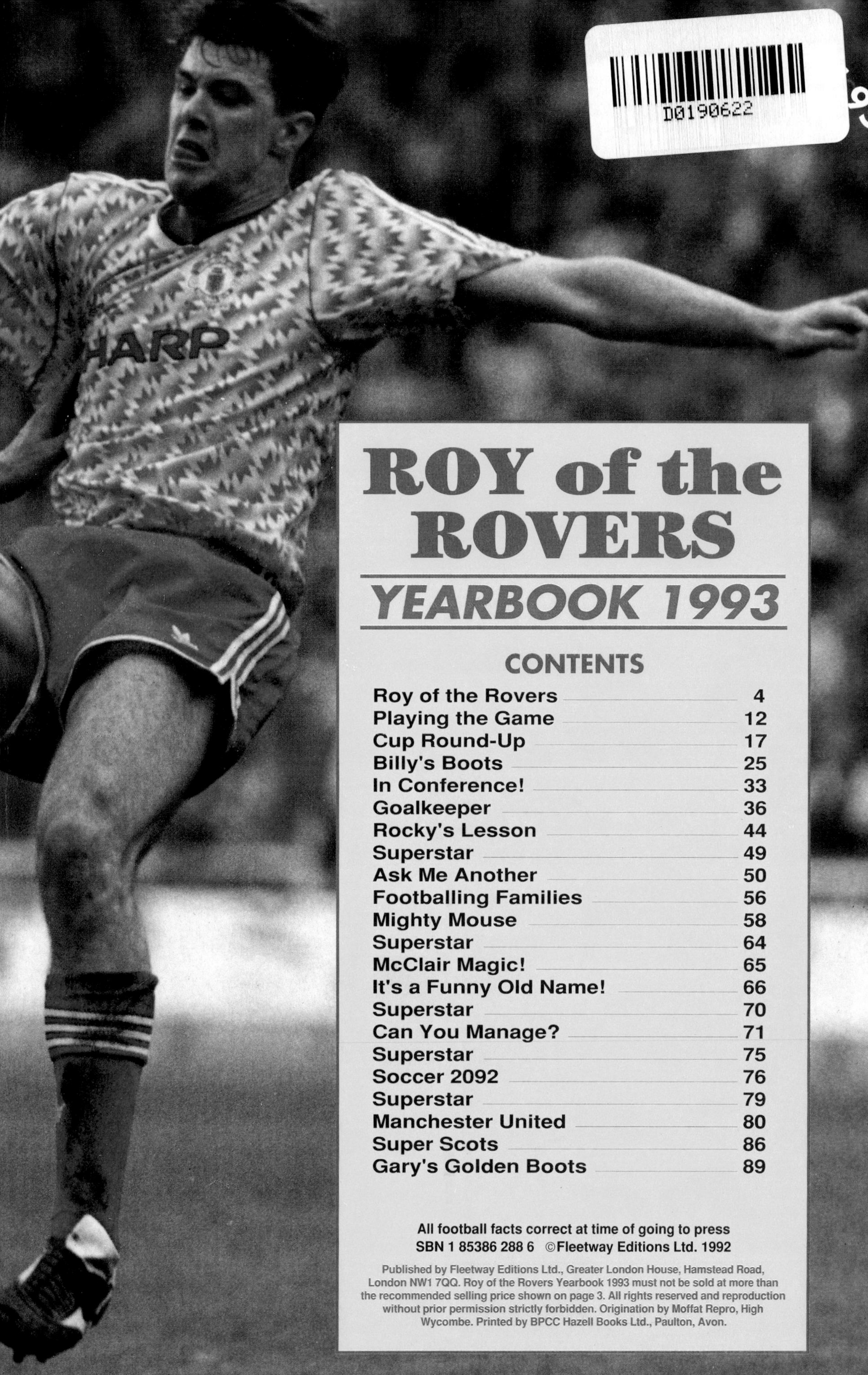

ROY of the ROVERS

YEARBOOK 1993

CONTENTS

Roy of the Rovers 4
Playing the Game 12
Cup Round-Up 17
Billy's Boots 25
In Conference! 33
Goalkeeper 36
Rocky's Lesson 44
Superstar 49
Ask Me Another 50
Footballing Families 56
Mighty Mouse 58
Superstar 64
McClair Magic! 65
It's a Funny Old Name! 66
Superstar 70
Can You Manage? 71
Superstar 75
Soccer 2092 76
Superstar 79
Manchester United 80
Super Scots 86
Gary's Golden Boots 89

All football facts correct at time of going to press

SBN 1 85386 288 6

Published by Fleetway Editions Ltd., Greater London House, Hamstead Road, London NW1 7QQ. Roy of the Rovers Yearbook 1993 must not be sold at more than the recommended selling price shown on page 3. Origination by Moffat Repro, High Wycombe. Printed by BPCC Hazell Books Ltd., Paulton, Avon.

Roy of the Rovers
ROM ROM ROMANA!
ROY RACE, PLAYER-MANAGER OF FIRST DIVISION MELCHESTER ROVERS, WAS SHOWING HIS TEAM A VIDEO RE-RUN OF THEIR FIRST LEG HOME MATCH IN THE SECOND ROUND OF THE UEFA CUP AGAINST TOP ITALIAN SIDE APOLLO ROMANA.
LISTEN TO THOSE ITALIAN SUPPORTERS! TWO THOUSAND OF THEM MADE THE TRIP AND IT FEELS LIKE TWENTY THOUSAND!
APOLLO FANS ARE FOOTBALL FANATICS! THEY MAKE THE BIGGEST NOISE IN SOCCER!
FORGET THE FANS, CONCENTRATE ON THE SCREEN! IT'S POST-MORTEM TIME, REMEMBER?
YEAH, THIS WAS PROBABLY OUR MOST IMPORTANT GAME OF THE SEASON ...
"WE HAD A BRILLIANT START WHEN OLLY OLSEN BROKE LOOSE ON THE RIGHT!"
YOURS, ALEX! ON YOUR OWN!

GNNFFF!
A PEACH OF A MOVE! RITCHIE'S PAST TWO OF 'EM!
GIVE IT THE HAMMER, SON!
YESSSSSSSS!
THAT'S THE EARLY GOAL WE WANTED, LADS! NOW KEEP THE PRESSURE UP!
FOR THE NEXT HALF-HOUR IT WAS ONE-WAY TRAFFIC! WE COULDN'T DO A THING WRONG!
THERE'S RACEY PICKING UP A HIGH BALL FROM NOBBY WOOTTEN! REMEMBER THAT MOVE, BOSS?
YOU BET! IT SHOULD HAVE BEEN GOAL NUMBER TWO, BUT I WAS A FRACTION OFF TARGET!
"IT WAS PURE 'MELCHESTER MAGIC' RIGHT UP UNTIL HALF-TIME! ONLY SHEER BAD LUCK KEPT THE BALL OUT OF THE ITALIAN NET!"
ANOTHER FLUKEY SAVE! WE SHOULD BE AT LEAST THREE UP BY NOW!
NO SWEAT, ROY! AFTER THE BREAK WE'LL GO OUT AND BURY THIS LOT!

I THOUGHT SO TOO... BUT WHAT HAPPENED INSTEAD?
WE-ER-MESSED THINGS UP, BOSS! LOST CONCENTRATION...

YOU DID MORE THAN THAT! YOU SAT BACK AND RELAXED... LOST POSSESSION IN MID-FIELD, LOST POSSESSION EVERYWHERE!

"EVERY APOLLO ATTACK WAS LED BY THEIR CAPTAIN... CARLO MANCINI. HE'S A HARDMAN WITH A LOT OF SKILLS..."
"...THE BIGGEST NAME IN ITALIAN FOOTBALL!"
MAN-CINI... MAN-CINI... MAN-CINI!
BRAVISSIMO... CARLO'S THROUGH!

ROMANA
MELCHESTER ROVERS...1
APOLLO ROMANA......1

SWITCH THAT THING OFF, BOSS, I DON'T THINK I CAN WATCH ANY MORE!
YOU'LL WATCH IT, BRUNO... YOU'LL ALL WATCH IT AND SEE JUST HOW BADLY YOU PLAYED IN THE SECOND HALF.

WE COULD HAVE LOST THREE OR EVEN FOUR-ONE... IF IT HADN'T BEEN FOR ONE MAN! ANDY STYLES!
ROY'S RIGHT, ANDY... YOU PLAYED A BLINDER THAT DAY!

"WHILE WE WERE SHUFFLING ABOUT LIKE TAILORS' DUMMIES, YOU SAVED OUR BACON TIME AND AGAIN!"

FINAL SCORE 1-1! INSTEAD OF GOING TO ITALY FOR THE SECOND LEG WITH A COMFORTABLE LEAD, WE'LL BE OUT THERE IN THE THUNDERBOWL FIGHTING FOR OUR LIVES!
OUT THERE IN THE WHAT?

THUNDERBOWL! THAT'S APOLLO'S STADIUM! LIGHTNING-FAST FOOTBALL ON THE FIELD, A STORM OF SOUND FROM THE TERRACES!
AYE... THEY RECKON THOSE ITALIAN FANS MAKE THE HAMPDEN ROAR SOUND LIKE A DRY COUGH!

IF TWO THOUSAND CAN MAKE A DIN LIKE THAT, IMAGINE WHAT SIXTY THOUSAND WILL BE LIKE!
ALL I WANT OUT OF YOU LOT FOR THE RETURN MATCH IS ONE HUNDRED PER CENT EFFORT! AS I SAID BEFORE... FORGET THE FANS!

BUT ON THE NIGHT OF THE BIG GAME, EVEN ROY HAD TO ADMIT THAT WAS EASIER SAID THAN DONE!
ROM-ROM ROMANA!
WE'VE PLAYED BEFORE HOSTILE CROWDS BEFORE, BUT THIS IS SOME-THING ELSE!
IN NINETY MINUTES YOU'LL BE OUT OF THE UEFA CUP, SIGNOR RACE!

LAST TIME YOUR GOALKEEPER SAVED YOU! IT WON'T HAPPEN TONIGHT!
NOT A CHANCE! HA, HA, HA!
I WONDER WHAT THE HECK *THAT'S* SUPPOSED TO MEAN?

KICK-OFF!
ROM-ROM-ROM... ROMANAAAAA!
APOLLO HAVE PUSHED EVERYONE UP! WHAT ARE THEY TRYING TO DO?
STEAMROLLER US IN THE FIRST HALF HOUR! I TOLD YOU WE'D BE OUT HERE FIGHTING FOR OUR LIVES!

THE ITALIANS FORCED THREE CORNERS IN QUICK SUCCESSION. THEN...
AAAAGH!
ANDY! WHAT'S UP?

G-GOT THUMPED IN THE BACK! PROBABLY JUST AN ACCIDENT. I'M OKAY!

BUT WHEN TWO *MORE* "ACCIDENTS" HAPPENED IN THE SPACE OF FIFTEEN MINUTES...
NOW I GET IT! MANCINI AND HIS MEN ARE GIVING ANDY 'THE TREATMENT'! THEY RECKON THAT IF HE CRACKS, THE *REST* OF US WILL CRACK TOO!
UUUUGH!

WELL, MAYBE IT'S TIME TO STICK A SPANNER IN THEIR WORKS!
ANDY... MY BALL!

THAT'S A WASTED RUN, ROY! YOU'RE ON YOUR OWN, NO BACK-UP!
I DON'T NEED ANY! THE APOLLO 'KEEPER IS MILES OFF HIS LINE...

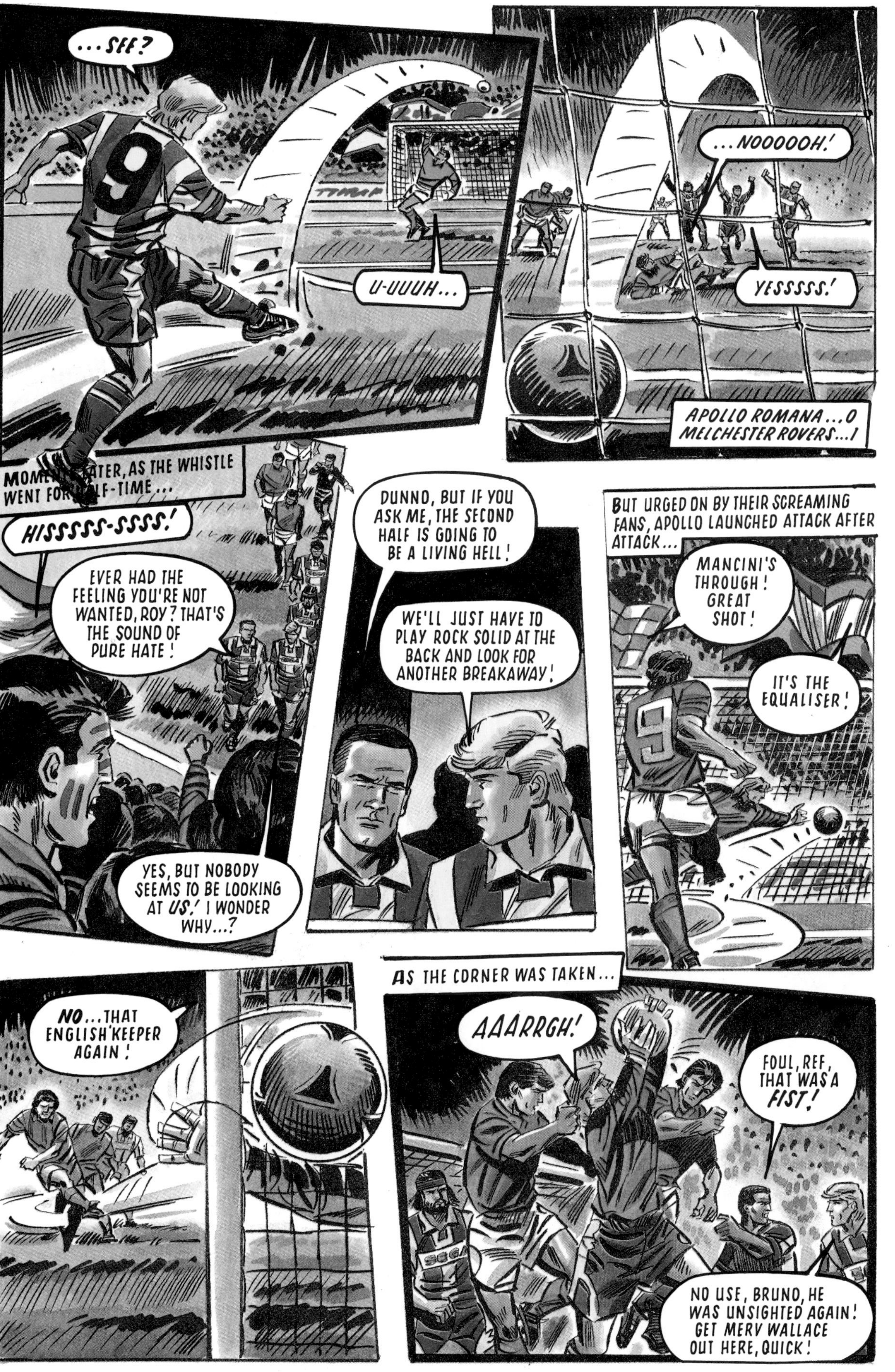

...SEE?

U-UUUH...

...NOOOOOH!

YESSSSS!

APOLLO ROMANA...0 MELCHESTER ROVERS...1

MOMENTS LATER, AS THE WHISTLE WENT FOR HALF-TIME...

HISSSSS-SSSS!

EVER HAD THE FEELING YOU'RE NOT WANTED, ROY? THAT'S THE SOUND OF PURE HATE!

YES, BUT NOBODY SEEMS TO BE LOOKING AT *US!* I WONDER WHY...?

DUNNO, BUT IF YOU ASK ME, THE SECOND HALF IS GOING TO BE A LIVING HELL!

WE'LL JUST HAVE TO PLAY ROCK SOLID AT THE BACK AND LOOK FOR ANOTHER BREAKAWAY!

BUT URGED ON BY THEIR SCREAMING FANS, APOLLO LAUNCHED ATTACK AFTER ATTACK...

MANCINI'S THROUGH! GREAT SHOT!

IT'S THE EQUALISER!

AS THE CORNER WAS TAKEN...

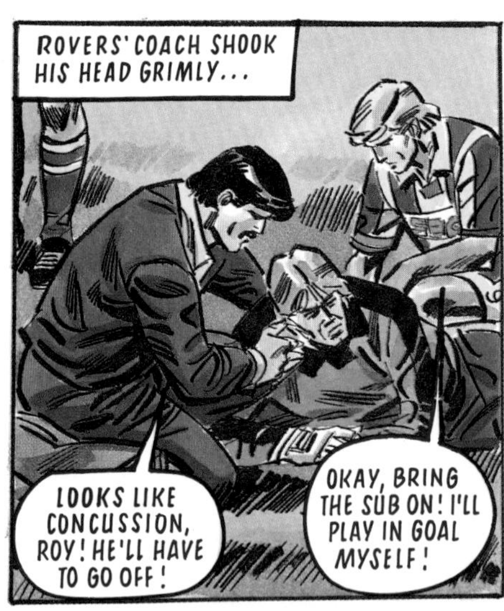
ROVERS' COACH SHOOK HIS HEAD GRIMLY...
LOOKS LIKE CONCUSSION, ROY! HE'LL HAVE TO GO OFF!
OKAY, BRING THE SUB ON! I'LL PLAY IN GOAL MYSELF!

THAT'S A BAD MOVE, ROY, WE NEED YOU UP FRONT!
NOT ANY MORE! WHAT WE NEED NOW IS DEFENCE! HANG ON TO THIS ONE-GOAL LEAD AND WE'RE THROUGH ON AGGREGATE!

AND HANG ON THEY DID...
BIG JOHNNY DEXTER WENT IN... TOO HARD!
AAAAAH!
PENALTY!

...UNTIL JUST ONE MINUTE FROM FULL-TIME...
DUNC'S FLUFFED A CLEARANCE! THEIR WINGER'S THROUGH!
NOT YET HE AIN'T!

AN EERIE HUSH DESCENDED ON THE VAST STADIUM...
IF THEY SCORE THIS, THE GAME WILL GO INTO EXTRA-TIME...AND NO WAY WE'LL SURVIVE THAT!
CARLO MANCINI'S GOING TO TAKE THE KICK! WHAT'S ROY UP TO..?

WHAT'S HE TALKING TO MANCINI ABOUT?
HOW THE HECK SHOULD I KNOW?

SECONDS LATER...
I CAN'T LOOK, OLLY... I JUST CAN'T!
A ROCKET! ROY HASN'T EVEN MOVED, IT'S A G—

NO... OVER THE BAR! HE MISSED!
THERE'S THE WHISTLE! WE'RE THROUGH!

HISSSSS-SSSS-SSS!
HOW COME HE FLUFFED IT, ROY? WHAT HAPPENED?
I SUDDENLY REMEMBERED THE CROWD AT HALF-TIME! THEY WEREN'T HISSING US FOR SCORING, THEY WERE HISSING THEIR OWN TEAM FOR ALLOWING US TO SCORE!

THE THUNDERBOWL FANS ARE SO FANATICAL THEY CAN'T STAND TO SEE THEIR SIDE LOSE!

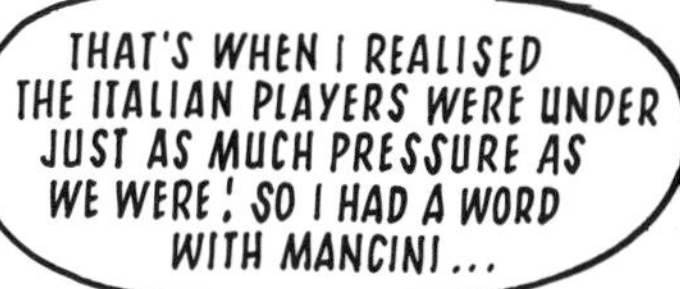
THAT'S WHEN I REALISED THE ITALIAN PLAYERS WERE UNDER JUST AS MUCH PRESSURE AS WE WERE! SO I HAD A WORD WITH MANCINI...

THE FANS ARE WAITING FOR YOU TO BANG THIS HOME, CARLO! I HOPE YOU DON'T LET THEM DOWN!

BETTER KEEP A COOL HEAD, PAL...
...BETTER NOT MISS!

BUT HE DID! HIS NERVE CRACKED! THE BIGGER THEY ARE, THE HARDER THEY FALL! THAT'S WHAT FOOTBALL'S ALL ABOUT!
SEGA
SEGA
THE END

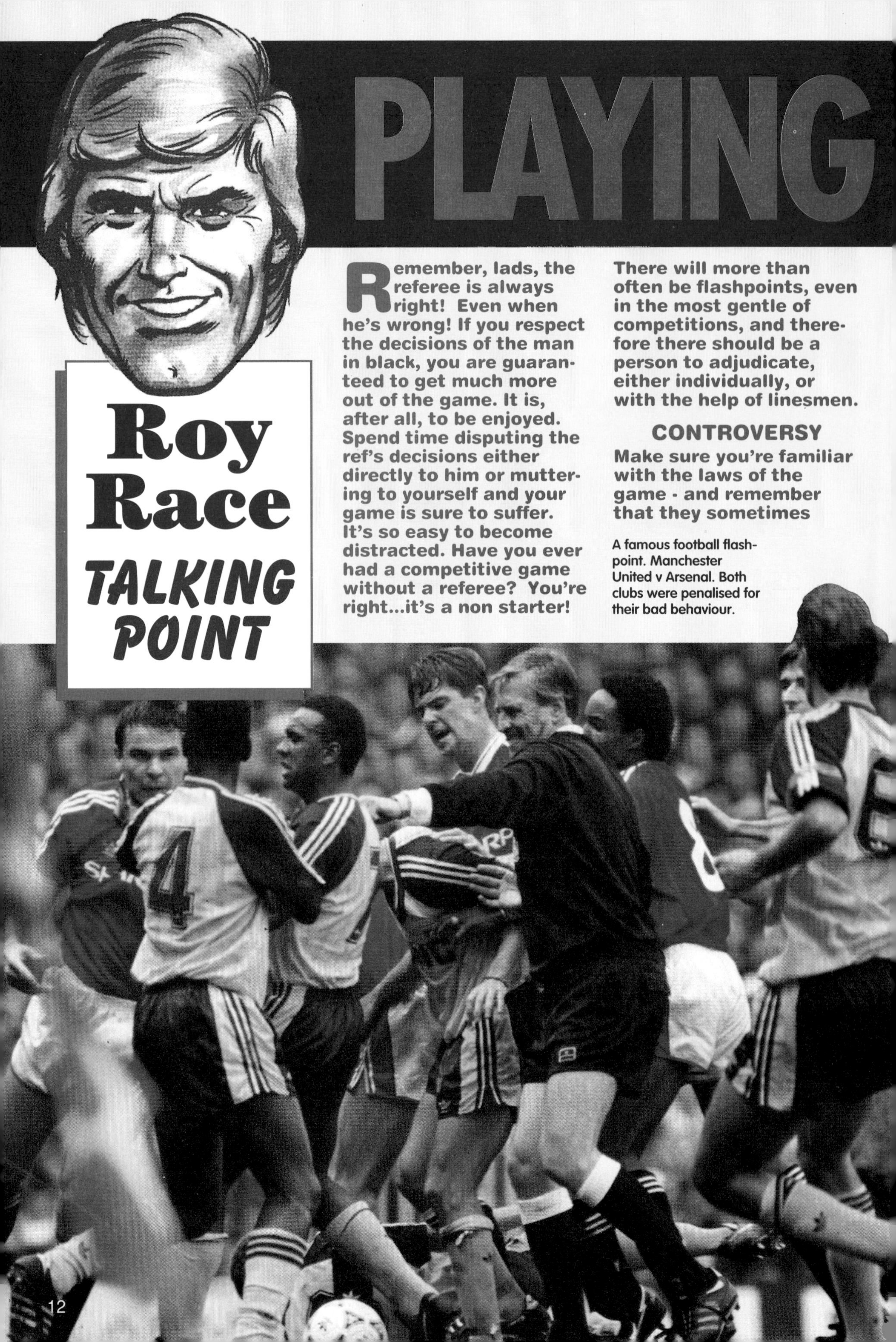

PLAYING

Roy Race

TALKING POINT

Remember, lads, the referee is always right! Even when he's wrong! If you respect the decisions of the man in black, you are guaranteed to get much more out of the game. It is, after all, to be enjoyed. Spend time disputing the ref's decisions either directly to him or muttering to yourself and your game is sure to suffer. It's so easy to become distracted. Have you ever had a competitive game without a referee? You're right...it's a non starter!

There will more than often be flashpoints, even in the most gentle of competitions, and therefore there should be a person to adjudicate, either individually, or with the help of linesmen.

CONTROVERSY

Make sure you're familiar with the laws of the game - and remember that they sometimes

A famous football flashpoint. Manchester United v Arsenal. Both clubs were penalised for their bad behaviour.

THE GAME!

Not enjoying your football like you used to? Here are a few words of advice and encouragement from Roy Race!

change from season to season. After the 1990 World Cup, two important rule changes were introduced by the International Board. The professional foul was outlawed. This meant that any player deliberately stopping an opponent with a clear run on goal was to be sent off - shown the red card. As I explain later, referees are allowed to use their discretion, and in some circumstances, a booking - a yellow card - or a warning can suffice. In the professional game this has served to increase, rather than reduce, controversy. Basically, the law change favours fowards and should create more goalscoring chances in a match.

The other major change was in the offside law - always a problem area for players and referees alike. Under the new ruling, players are onside if they are IN LINE with the last defender. Previously, in line meant that the attackers were offside. Basically, they have to time their runs from behind the defensive players. If you watch Gary Lineker closely, he generally has this art down to perfection!

Foul play, of course, cannot be tolerated. Football is a tough, physical contact sport, but it can still be played in good spirit. Hard, but fair, can be used to describe the majority of defenders in Britain.

Bad behaviour on the park gets the ultimate reward - the red card from the man in black. Here - hidden by the referee - is Spurs' Nayim.

PLAYING THE GAME!

AGGRESSION

Of course, one of the worst fouls in the modern game is the tackle from behind, particularly when a player has just released the ball. Then there is the 'over the top' tackle where a player will pass his foot over the ball and deliberately make contact with his rival. Goalkeepers charging from goal to collect a cross with their foot outstretched is another example of unjustified aggression. Firm referees will act swiftly to combat these examples of unfair play.

Retaliation is something to avoid at all costs. If you have received a painful kick or, worse still, a sly punch, or push, out of the officials' vision, there may be a split-second urge to get your own back. In one word...DON'T! The original victim, as opposed to the perpetrator, can often become the guilty party. Referees will rightly punish players trying to take the law into their own hands.

Then there is gamesmanship. This is where players try to gain an unfair advantage outside the laws. Players not retreating ten yards at free-kicks is a common one. Feigning injury is another 'trick' to either implicate a rival player or cover up a bad tackle. Then there is dissent. Remember, lads, it's better to keep your thoughts to yourself, because there is a danger that comments aimed at another player could be misinterpreted by the official as referring to him!

I don't want to dwell too long on the negative aspects of our great game, but I believe that outlining the most common examples of unfair play, proves that cheats cannot prosper. They will be caught out eventually. Players with a bad attitude and poor discipline always pay the penalty - if they miss games through suspension and word travels fast throughout the game that they are ones to 'watch' closely.

INJURY

Sportsmanship is alive and well in football. I applaud the trend in recent years of players kicking the ball out of play when an opponent is injured. It is then returned to the team when play is resumed.

I know I have already mentioned Gary Lineker,

but he is a shining example to youngsters with his refusal to be intimidated. His record of never being booked is a tribute to his temperament. Nice guy though Gary is, it hasn't stopped defenders trying to carve lumps out of him. He played for two years with Barcelona in the Spanish League, one of the toughest in the world. And I still shudder at some of the tackles he has taken in the white shirt of England, particularly during the 1990 World Cup.

MEMORABLE

Again, though, there was an example of how the bad boys won't get their way. Lineker came in for some tough treatment from Cameroon defenders in the World Cup quarter-final, but they eventually gave away two penalties through fouls on him. Gary made them pay by converting both to seal England's memorable 3-2 victory.

Most of us remember the last World Cup and how close England came to toppling Germany, the eventual winners. Sadly, I also remember what an ill-disciplined shambles the final became, with two Argentinian players sent off as Germany took the world crown, courtesy

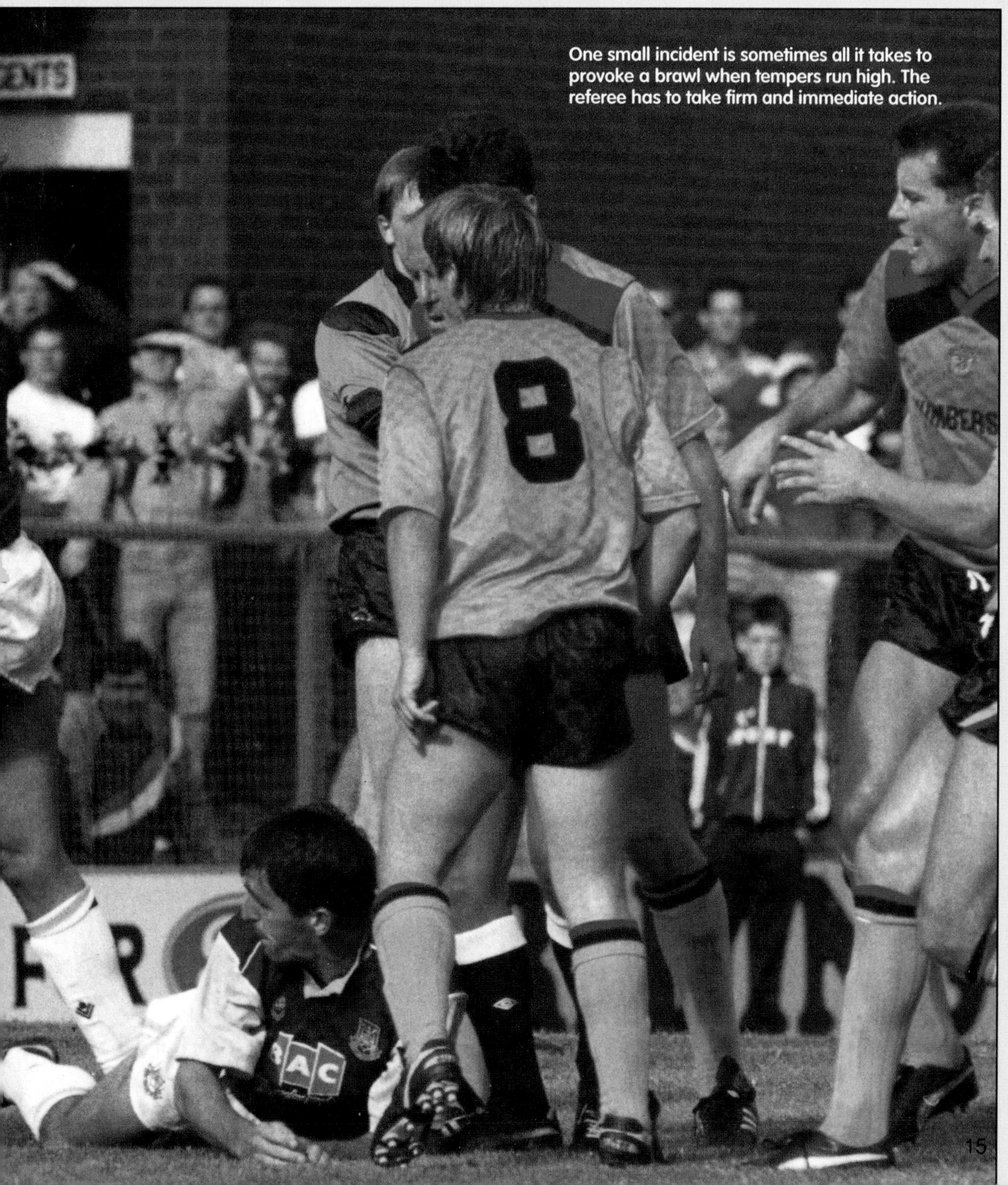

One small incident is sometimes all it takes to provoke a brawl when tempers run high. The referee has to take firm and immediate action.

PLAYING THE GAME!

of a disputed penalty five minutes from time.

The law changes after the World Cup, which I mentioned earlier, have certainly sparked some debate in our professional game.

The outcome of the 1990-91 FA Cup semi-final between Nottingham Forest and West Ham was virtually decided by a 'professional foul' judgement from referee Keith Hackett.

When West Ham defender Tony Gale baulked Forest winger Gary Crosby a few yards from goal, Mr Hackett ruled it a professional foul and sent off the West Ham player. Similar offences in other matches have resulted in a yellow card for the offender. West Ham, reduced to 10 men for 75 minutes, eventually crumbled and lost the match 4-0.

DISMISSAL

George Courtney, another of England's leading officials, found himself on the spot after his dismissal of Jimmy Case, then of Southampton, for a professional foul in a Rumbelows Cup match at Old Trafford. Weeks later, with Mr Courtney again in charge, he chose merely to book John McClelland of Leeds for committing what seemed to be an identical offence in an FA Cup match against Barnsley.

Both incidents were caught by the TV cameras - and much discussion followed, not all of it in the referee's favour. The referee's lot may not appear to be a happy one, but as George says: "You're always going to upset someone. The important thing is to make your decisions and stick to them - don't waver."

The F.A. expects high standards from professional players and if they make gestures to fans, they will be in trouble. Sportsmanship, though, isn't restricted to players. Supporters have to play their part as well. Referees don't expect crowds to chant their names in salute, but remember they're only human and they can make mistakes. It would be a poor old game without them!

A police presence is necessary because of trouble between opposing fans. Fortunately, behaviour on the terraces is improving.

BARCLAYS LEAGUE DIVISION ONE CHAMPIONSHIP – WINNERS LEEDS UTD.

Champions!

A delighted Gordon Strachan holds aloft the League Championship trophy before Leeds United's last match of the season against Norwich City at Elland Road.

Leeds United became the champions of the Barclays League after a thrilling season-long battle with Manchester United.

The title race was finally decided with just one game to spare as Leeds won 3-2 at Sheffield United while Manchester United were beaten at Liverpool.

There was obvious tension on the Leeds bench during their match at Sheffield (below) but the pressure was off as Gordon Strachan received the Championship trophy before the last game against Norwich City (left).

And the whole Leeds side were in the mood for celebrating as they showed off their riches in front of their fans (bottom).

SCOTTISH PREMIER CHAMPIONSHIP AND CUP WINNERS – RANGERS

SCOTS AT THE DOUBLE

In Scotland, Rangers carried off a League and Cup double.

Pictured are (from left) Iain Durant, Gary Stevens, Stuart McCall and Nigel Spackman celebrating with the Premier Division Championship trophy after a 4-0 win over St. Mirren.

Rangers completed the double with a 2-1 victory over Airdrie in the Scottish Cup final.

ROVERS RETURN!

A last-gasp win over Leicester in the play-offs secured Blackburn and manager Kenny Dalglish a spot in the new Premier League next season. Well done, lads!

CHAMPIONS!

DIVISION 2 – IPSWICH TOWN

DIVISION 3 – BRENTFORD DIVISION 4 BURNLEY

U.E.F.A. CUP FINAL – WINNERS AJAX

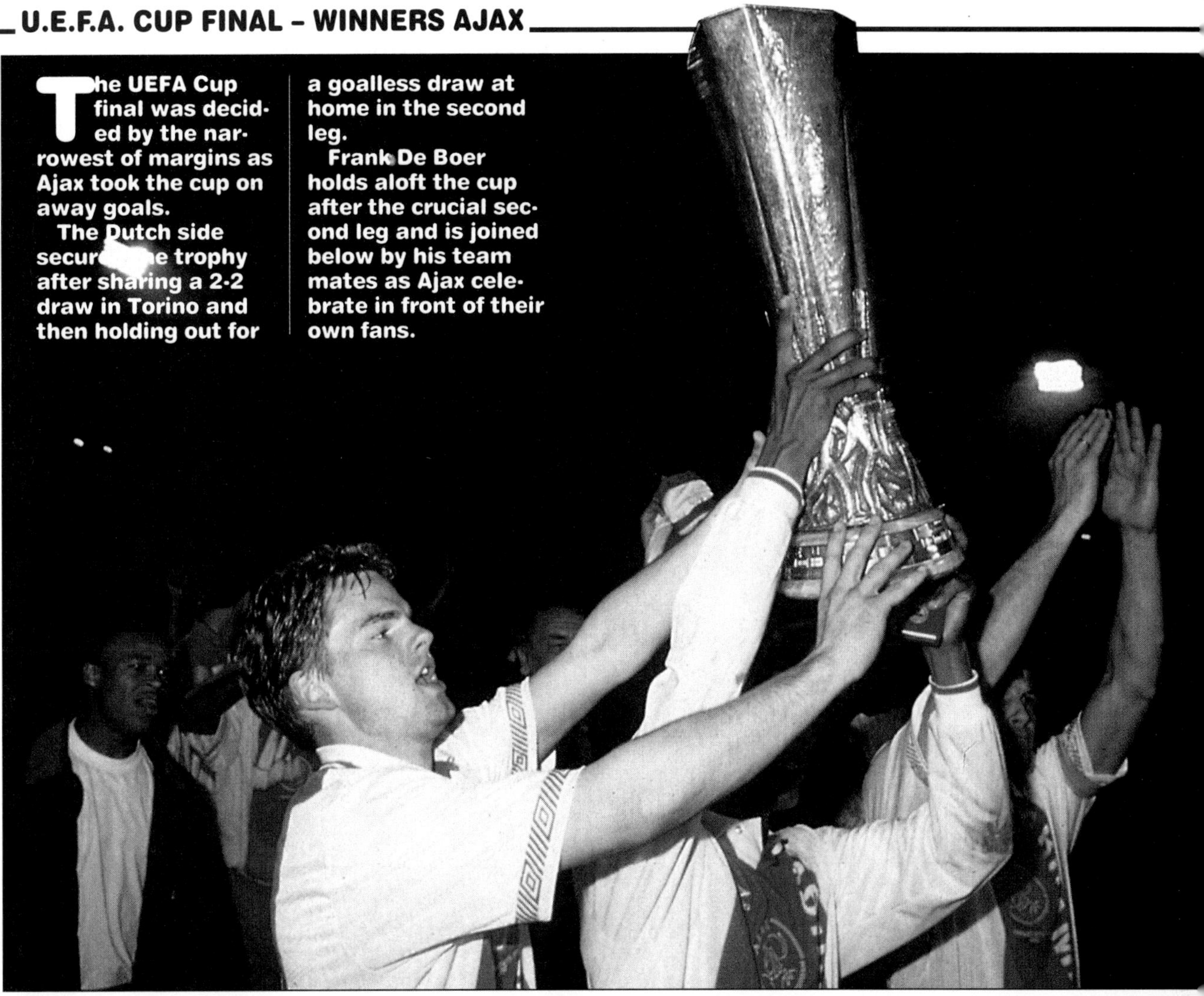

The UEFA Cup final was decided by the narrowest of margins as Ajax took the cup on away goals.

The Dutch side secured the trophy after sharing a 2-2 draw in Torino and then holding out for a goalless draw at home in the second leg.

Frank De Boer holds aloft the cup after the crucial second leg and is joined below by his team mates as Ajax celebrate in front of their own fans.

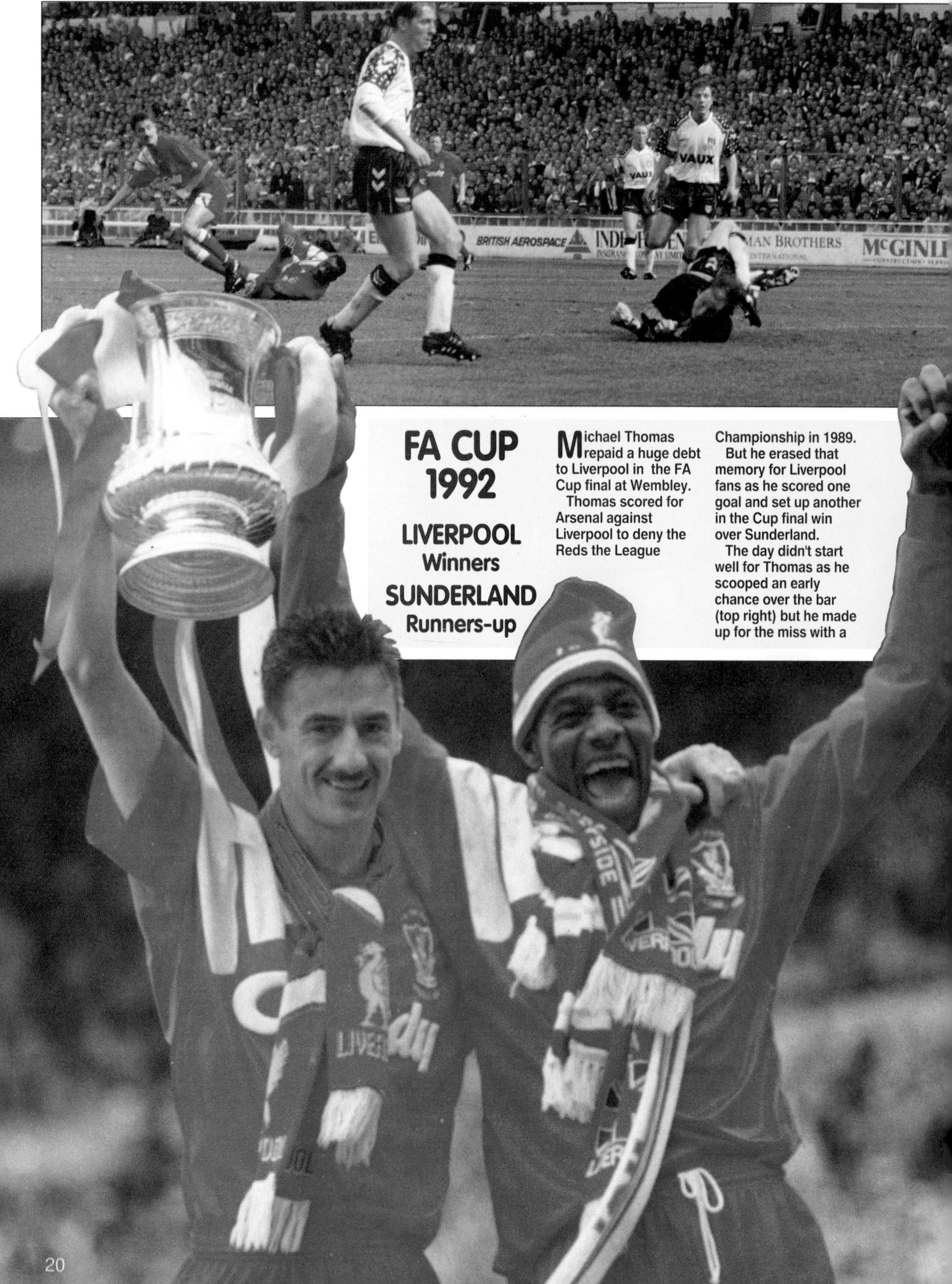

FA CUP 1992

LIVERPOOL
Winners
SUNDERLAND
Runners-up

Michael Thomas repaid a huge debt to Liverpool in the FA Cup final at Wembley.

Thomas scored for Arsenal against Liverpool to deny the Reds the League Championship in 1989.

But he erased that memory for Liverpool fans as he scored one goal and set up another in the Cup final win over Sunderland.

The day didn't start well for Thomas as he scooped an early chance over the bar (top right) but he made up for the miss with a

spectacular volley to open the scoring.

And Thomas then set up Ian Rush for Liverpool's all-important second goal (top left). The goalscorers are pictured (bottom left) celebrating with the FA Cup before joining their team mates (bottom right) for the traditional Wembley pose.

BRUCIE BONUS

Liverpool's clown prince goalkeeper, Bruce Grobbelaar, celebrates with team mate Jan Molby after the Mersey giants had beaten Sunderland 2-0 in the FA Cup final at Wembley in May.

The win maintained Liverpool's interest in European competitions as their victory over the second division side sealed a place in next season's Cup Winners Cup.

EUROPEAN CUP FINAL 1992 – WINNERS BARCELONA

Spanish club Barcelona edged to a 1-0 extra time win over Italian champions Sampdoria in the European Cup final.

The match, played at Wembley stadium, was won by a fierce strike by Dutchman Ronald Koeman, who blasted home following a free kick just outside the penalty area.

Koeman is pictured (below) cracking home the winning goal and other pictures show: bottom right – the winning Barcelona side celebrate their victory after a gruelling two hours of football; bottom left – victorious Barcelona coach Johan Cruyff watches anxiously during the match; left – Barcelona skipper Jose Alesanco holds aloft the European Cup.

EUROPEAN CUP WINNERS CUP FINAL – WINNERS WERDER BREMEN

Werder Bremen striker Wynton Rufer sprints off in celebration (below) after scoring his side's crucial second goal in the European Cup Winners Cup final in Lisbon, Portugal.

The New Zealand born striker's goal sealed a 2-0 victory for the Germans over fancied French side Monaco in May's final.

Rufer and his Werder Bremen team mates are pictured (bottom) celebrating their victory while Werder's delighted captain Mirko Votava (left) holds aloft the treasured silverware.

BILLY'S BOOTS
CAN YOU IMAGINE RUNNING OUT OF THIS TUNNEL AS A TOP PROFESSIONAL ONE DAY, BILLY?
BILLY DANE OWNED A PAIR OF OLD FOOTBALL BOOTS THAT USED TO BELONG TO A FAMOUS PLAYER FROM THE PAST CALLED 'DEAD-SHOT' KEEN. . .AND IN SOME STRANGE WAY THE BOOTS ENABLED BILLY TO PLAY WELL. IN THE LOCAL DERBY MATCH BETWEEN HIGHFIELD AND SHENTON UNITED, BILLY AND SOME OF HIS PALS FROM THE FARM YOUTH CLUB, HAD BEEN SELECTED AS BALL-BOYS FOR THE GAME. . .
YOU BET! THIS IS A FABULOUS HONOUR.

HIGHFIELD! HIGHFIELD! HIGHFIELD!
WHAT AN ATMOSPHERE! IT'S A FULL-HOUSE TODAY, SO LET'S HOPE THE GAME IS A GOOD ONE!

HIGHFIELD, STRUGGLING NEAR THE BOTTOM OF THE FIRST DIVISION AND DESPERATELY NEEDING POINTS, STARTED WELL WHEN THE GAME BEGAN. . .
GREAT BALL! NOW SLING IT INTO THE MIDDLE. . .
SHENTON'S DEFENCE IS ALL OVER THE PLACE.

BUT. . .
NAH. . .FORD NEVER LOOKED LIKE GETTING TO THAT ONE!
ANOTHER CHANCE WASTED!
HE'S THE REASON WE'RE HAVING SUCH A BAD SEASON!

THEN. . .
SHENTON ARE AWAY!
THIS LOOKS DANGEROUS!
THE BARRACKING STEVE FORD IS GETTING FROM THE FANS HAS BADLY AFFECTED HIS CONFIDENCE. HE HASN'T SCORED FOR THREE MONTHS NOW!

THE SHENTON BREAK WAS A GOOD ONE...
GREAT BALL!
IT'S GOT TO BE NUMBER ONE...

GOAL! FIRST BLOOD TO SHENTON!
I DON'T BELIEVE IT! THE MOVE BREAKS DOWN BECAUSE OF FORD AND SECONDS LATER WE'RE TRAILING
WHY DOESN'T THE MANAGER BRING ON THE SUB IN HIS PLACE?

LATER IN THE GAME...
THAT'S ALL YOUR FIT FOR, FORD... TAKING THE THROW-INS.
DON'T LET THEM GET TO YOU, MR. FORD. YOUR LUCK WILL RETURN.
THANKS, LAD!

BUT AT HALF-TIME, WITH HIGHFIELD STILL TRAILING 1-0...
BOOOO! DON'T BOTHER TO COME OUT FOR THE SECOND-HALF, FORD!
YEAH...WE'RE BETTER OFF WITHOUT YOU!
H.F.C.
CAN'T THEY SEE HE'S STRUGGLING TO FIND HIS FORM? HAVING A GO AT HIM DOESN'T HELP!

BUT IT WAS THE SAME STORY IN THE SECOND-HALF...
COME ON, FORD! MY GRANNY CAN JUMP HIGHER THAN THAT!
WHY DID HE BOTHER TO PUT HIS BOOTS ON TODAY?

THEN, AS BILLY WATCHED THE GAME...
HEY...DEAD-SHOT'S BOOTS ARE MAKING ME RUN TO THE RIGHT. I COULDN'T STOP MYSELF EVEN IF I WANTED TO!

THEN, ON THE FIELD, A SHENTON DEFENDER MISKICKED WILDLY...
OOOOH! THAT'LL HAVE ICE ON IT WHEN IT COMES DOWN!

THANKS TO HIS SUDDEN RUN, BILLY WAS IN A PERFECT POSITION TO CATCH THE BALL. . .
WELL SAVED, THE BALL–BOY!

AND. . .
QUICK, MR. FORD. THE BREAK'S ON IF YOU MOVE FAST.

AND, WITH THE SHENTON DEFENCE TOO FAR FORWARD. . .
YOURS, JIMMY!
HEY. . .THIS LOOKS INTERESTING! FORD'S QUICK THROW HAS GIVEN US A GREAT CHANCE!

THE HIGHFIELD FORWARD CUT IN WITH ONLY THE GOALIE TO BEAT. . .
GIVE IT A POKE, JIMMY!

BUT. . .
HE'S GIVEN IT TO FORD! WHAT A DAFT THING TO DO!
GOOOOOAAAALLLL!
FORD HAS BROKEN HIS DUCK! GREAT GOAL!
YEAH. . .HE STARTED AND FINISHED THAT MOVE!

THEN, TO BILLY'S SURPRISE...
THANKS, LITTLE MATE. WITHOUT YOUR HELP I'D STILL BE STRUGGLING OUT THERE!
I BET HE DOESN'T REALISE THAT IT WAS MY BOOTS WHO REALLY HELPED HIM!
WILL YOU LOOK AT THAT? FORD'S THANKING THE KID WHO GAVE HIM THE BALL FOR THE QUICK THROW. WELL DONE, YOUNGSTER!

AND WITH HIS CONFIDENCE RESTORED, STEVE FORD SCORED THE WINNING GOAL TEN MINUTES FROM TIME...
WHAT A GOAL! STEVE'S BACK ON FORM WITH A BANG!
TWO GOALS... THREE POINTS! GOOD OLD, STEVE!

LATER, AS BILLY LEFT THE GROUND...
HI–YA, BILLY!
WHO'S THAT?
HONK! HONK!

IT WAS STEVE FORD...
I'M GLAD I SAW YOU TO THANK YOU AGAIN. ANY FAVOUR I CAN DO FOR YOU IN RETURN, JUST ASK...
WELL, ER... THERE IS ONE!

OUR YOUTH CLUB MANAGER HAS TO GO AWAY ON URGENT BUSINESS. AND AS WE'RE PLAYING THE TOP TEAM IN A LEAGUE DECIDER ON WEDNESDAY EVENING, I WAS THINKING...
THAT I MIGHT BECOME YOUR MANAGER FOR A COUPLE OF DAYS. CONSIDER IT A FAVOUR, LITTLE MATE.

AND, WHEN BILLY AND HIS FARM TEAM-MATES REPORTED FOR TRAINING...
HI, KIDS. IF YOU THINK IT'S GOING TO BE EASY WITH ME IN CHARGE...THEN YOU'D BETTER THINK AGAIN.
HEY, IT'S STEVE FORD. WE THOUGHT BILLY WAS KIDDING US!
SEE, I TOLD YOU!

STEVE PUT THEM THROUGH THEIR PACES...
FASTER! FASTER!

THAT'S IT... A NICE, EASY LIFT!

THIS IS WORSE THAN 'IT'S A KNOCKOUT'!

AT THE END...
FROM WHAT BILLY'S TOLD ME, YOU HAVE A COUPLE OF YOUR BEST PLAYERS OUT THROUGH INJURY. SO TRY TO CONTAIN THEM AT THE START...BUT ALL THE TIME BE ON THE LOOK-OUT FOR FAST COUNTER-ATTACKS!

UNFORTUNATELY, I MIGHT NOT BE HERE IN TIME TO SEE YOU IN ACTION TOMORROW EVENING. SO JUST IN CASE I DON'T MAKE IT, I'LL WISH YOU ALL THE BEST NOW.
THANKS, STEVE.
YEAH! THAT WAS THE BEST TRAINING SESSION WE EVER HAD!

IN BED THAT NIGHT, BILLY READ FROM HIS BOOK ON DEAD-SHOT'S LIFE-STORY...
HERE'S A PIECE ABOUT DEAD-SHOT ONCE PLAYING FOR HIS YOUTH CLUB IN A LEAGUE DECIDER...BUT THERE'S NOTHING ABOUT A PROFESSIONAL PLAYER HELPING THEM...

BILLY READ ON. . .
'DEAD–SHOT'S UNCLE SID TOOK A KEEN INTEREST IN ALL HIS MATCHES AND HARDLY EVER MISSED A GAME. . .'
GO ON, SON. . . ALL THE WAY!

'AND HIS BOOMING VOICE SEEMED TO INSPIRE DEAD–SHOT TO PLAY WELL. . .'
THAT'S GOOD! NOW GIVE IT A POKE, LAD. . .

'AND, THANKS TO HIS UNCLE'S MOTIVATION, DEAD–SHOT SCORED TWO LATE GOALS TO CLINCH THE LEAGUE TITLE FOR HIS YOUTH SIDE.'
GOAAAALLLLL!
GOOD OLD DEAD–SHOT!

WELL, EVEN THOUGH A LOT OF THINGS THAT HAPPENED TO DEAD–SHOT SEEM TO HAPPEN TO ME SINCE I STARTED WEARING HIS OLD BOOTS, I HAVEN'T GOT AN UNCLE WHO'LL TURN UP AND SHOUT ME ON TO VICTORY!

AND, IN THEIR VITAL GAME NEXT DAY, BILLY'S TEAM STRUGGLED AGAINST THE LEAGUE LEADERS, WHO ONLY NEEDED A POINT TO CLINCH THE CHAMPIONSHIP FROM FARM. . .
NITON ARE ALL OVER 'EM!
BUT DON'T FORGET THAT FARM HAVE TWO OF THEIR BEST PLAYERS OUT THROUGH INJURY.

BUT A GOAL HAD TO COME. . .
IT'S THERE! THE FIRST OF MANY!
FARM HAVE DEFENDED WELL. . .BUT IT WAS ONLY A MATTER OF TIME BEFORE THEY WENT UNDER!

1–0 WAS STILL THE SCORE AT HALF–TIME. . .
I'M WHACKED! IF STEVE HAD GOT HERE WE MIGHT HAVE STOOD A CHANCE!
WELL STEVE'S NOT HERE. . .SO WE CARRY ON AS WE'VE BEEN DOING. . .OUR BEST!

AND FARM CONTINUED TO DEFEND WELL. THEN, MIDWAY THROUGH THE SECOND PERIOD. . .
HEY. . .THE BOOTS SEEM TO BE MAKING ME MOVE UP INTO THE ATTACK.

BUT SUDDENLY THERE WAS A LOFTED CLEARANCE. . .
IT'S AN UP–AND–UNDER!

THERE'S ONLY ONE FARM BOY UP. . .
IF I CAN BRING IT UNDER CONTROL WHEN THE BALL BOUNCES. . .THEN I MUST HAVE A CHANCE.

BILLY BROUGHT THE BALL UNDER CONTROL. . .BRILLIANTLY!
GO ON, SON. . . NOW TAKE IT ALL THE WAY. . .
WHAT THE. . ? THAT LOUD VOICE. . . IT'S JUST LIKE IT HAPPENED IN DEAD–SHOT'S BOOK. . .

THE VOICE BELONGED TO STEVE FORD. . .
BRILLIANTLY AROUND THE GOALIE! YOU MUST SCORE, SON.

GOOOOAAAALLLLL!
WHAT A TURN UP. . .THE SCORES ARE LEVEL!
I COULD NEVER SEE FARM SCORING IN THIS MATCH!

GREAT GOAL, BILLY.
YEAH. . .AND NOW WE'VE GOT ONE WE CAN GET TWO!
IT WAS JUST AS IF STEVE'S SHOUT INSPIRED ME TO DO WELL!

THEIR TAILS UP, FARM PRESSED HARD FOR ANOTHER GOAL AND. . .
IT'S THERE! THAT BOY WITH THE OLD BOOTS IS MAGIC!
THE LEAGUE TITLE MUST BE FARM'S NOW! WHAT A CRAZY, TOPSY-TURVY GAME.

THE FINAL SCORE. . .FARM ATHLETIC 2, NITON 1.
THANKS FOR COMING, STEVE! IT MEANT A LOT TO ME I CAN TELL YOU!
SORRY I COULDN'T MAKE IT EARLIER. BY THE WAY, BILLY. . . WHY DO YOU PLAY IN THOSE OLD BOOTS?

BECAUSE THEY ONCE BELONGED TO A FAMOUS FOOTBALL STAR CALLED DEAD-SHOT KEEN. AND IN ANOTHER WAY THEY'RE VERY SPECIAL TO ME, BUT I CAN'T TELL YOU ABOUT THAT!

DEAD-SHOT KEEN? WHY, HE'S MY GREAT UNCLE. WHEN I WAS A KID, HE ALWAYS ENCOURAGED ME TO PLAY FOOTBALL. FANCY YOU KNOWING ABOUT DEAD-SHOT!

WELL, YOU'D NEVER BELIEVE IT. DEAD-SHOT'S UNCLE ONCE INSPIRED HIM TO PLAY WELL AND NOW STEVE, FROM THE KEEN FAMILY, HAS HELPED ME! THE STORY IN THE BOOK REPEATED ITSELF!

IT'S A FUNNY GAME FOOTBALL. . .BUT I BET EVERY BOY WISHED HE HAD A PAIR OF FOOTBALL BOOTS LIKE MINE TO HELP HIM!
The End

Bath City discovered Jason Dodd, who went on to play for Southampton, and Paul Bodin (below right) for Swindon and Wales.

A quick look at a breeding ground for talent

The Vauxhall Conference has been a rich breeding ground for players who have gone on to find fame and fortune.

And perhaps its two most famous graduates are currently captains of their countries...Stuart Pearce of England, and Andy Townsend of the Republic of Ireland.

Pearce began his career at Wealdstone, before moving to Coventry City and then Nottingham Forest where he has developed into one of the best left backs in the game.

IN CONFERENCE!

Mark Ward, once of West Ham, Man. City and now Everton began his footballing career at Northwich

He has been first choice in the number three shirt for three of the most demanding managers in the game, Brian Clough, Bobby Robson and Graham Taylor.

Pearce is certain, barring ill health or injury, to lead England into the 1994 World Cup Finals, and Taylor says of him:

"He has everything I want from a player and a captain. A great defender, leader, colleague and participant. Stuart is simply the best."

That's what Jack Charlton has been saying of Andy Townsend, who began his career with Welling, moved on to Weymouth, before stepping into the First Division with Southampton, Norwich and Chelsea.

One of the Conference's most charismatic starlets has been Vinny Jones, the ex hod-carrier who began his football with Wealdstone, and went on to become a cult figure in the game.

INSPIRATION

Jones, tough and uncompromising, scored in his first home game for Wimbledon against Manchester United.

And under the Dons' bright boss Harry Bassett, developed into a midfield player whose brawn as well as brain made him much in demand.

He was the inspiration of Wimbledon's 1988 F.A. Cup Final win over Liverpool that stunned football.

Then Vinny moved on to Leeds United and helped them win promotion to the First Division, before joining Bassett at Sheffield United where his spirit and leadership stopped them from going down.

Next stop was Chelsea. He says: "I learned in the Conference you had to work hard for anything you wanted. I like to think I'm a winner."

Others from the Conference are doing just as well. Shaun Teale of Aston Villa, started off with Northwich Victoria, and then Weymouth, before signing for Bournemouth, then moving to Villa for a million pounds.

Ian Woan of Nottingham Forest cut his early teeth at Runcorn, while Mark Ward, once of West Ham, Manchester City and now Everton also began at Northwich.

Bath City produced Jason Dodd for Southampton and the England "under 21" side, and also Paul Bodin for Bristol City, Crystal Palace, Swindon and Wales.

Tony Agana, now Notts County, was another off the productive Weymouth con-

Stuart Pearce is another famous name who started in the Vauxhall Conference. He should lead England into the 1994 World Cup Finals.

veyor belt, going to Watford before forging a dangerous strike pairing with Brian Deane at Sheffield United where they won promotion to the First Division.

TOP BOSSES

The Conference is studded with similar stars, and with top bosses who first took the long road to club management at the helm of little clubs.

Howard Wilkinson of Leeds was at Boston, so too was Jim Smith now Portsmouth, who managed Blackburn, Oxford, QPR, and Newcastle.

David Pleat, of

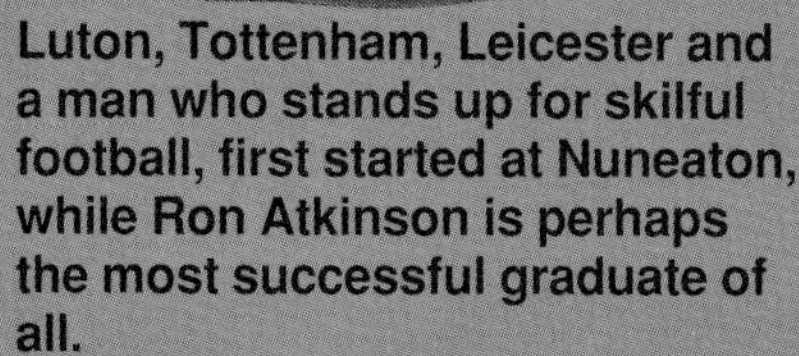

Luton, Tottenham, Leicester and a man who stands up for skilful football, first started at Nuneaton, while Ron Atkinson is perhaps the most successful graduate of all.

Big Ron bossed Kettering, before going on to Cambridge, West Bromwich, and Manchester United where he twice won the F.A. Cup, and then moving on to Sheffield Wednesday where he won the Rumbelows Cup, and promotion back to the First Division.

Now he is attempting to re-build Aston Villa after a mad whirl of transfer activity.

Colchester, Wycombe, Farnborough, Telford and Kettering have a pedigree rich in F.A. Cup tradition.

Both Farnborough and Kettering reached the third round proper of the competition, carrying the flag proudly for the Conference.

It has been a rich proving ground since its formation in 1979, and is certain to play a vital part in the future of the game.

The Conference is where it all begins, for players, for managers and coaches. That is why it continues to prosper and develop, and be so successful.

The unmistakable figure of Vinny Jones, currently with Chelsea. He started with Wealdstone.

TYNEFIELD CITY
Injury time!
TYNEFIELD CITY
FOOTBALL CLUB
GORDON STEWART
GOALKEEPER
DIED NOVEMBER 1983
HE GAVE PLEASURE
TO MANY
BRILLIANT YOUNG GOALKEEPER RICK STEWART WAS THE SON OF THE LATE, GREAT INTERNATIONAL GOALKEEPER GORDON STEWART, RENOWNED FOR HAVING THE SAFEST HANDS IN SOCCER...
GOALKEEPER

ONE OF RICK'S FAVOURITE HOBBIES WAS LOOKING THROUGH HIS FATHER'S COMPREHENSIVE SOCCER DIARY...
THIS IS FANTASTIC STUFF. DAD TOOK A NOTE OF EVERYTHING THAT HAPPENED TO HIM DURING HIS LONG CAREER.
SOCCER
Niggling injuries are an occupational hazard for footballers They're difficult for any player at the top level to avoid. At times like this, a good physio is worth his weight in gold.
I've been lucky so far...
AND WE KNOW WHY THAT IS! YOU, FRED! YOU WERE DAD'S LUCKY MASCOT, AND NOW YOU'RE MINE!
GOALKEEPER Soccer GORDON STEWART
IN FACT, TYNEFIELD CITY'S YOUTH TEAM WERE ENJOYING A SUCCESSFUL RUN...
A MARVELLOUS SAVE BY RICK STEWART!
WHAT A 'KEEPER! IT'S UNCANNY! JUST LIKE WATCHING HIS FATHER AGAIN!
RICK INSPIRES HIS TEAM MATES, THE SAME WAY AS GORDON USED TO!
NOT ONLY DID HE SAVE IT-HE HELD IT!

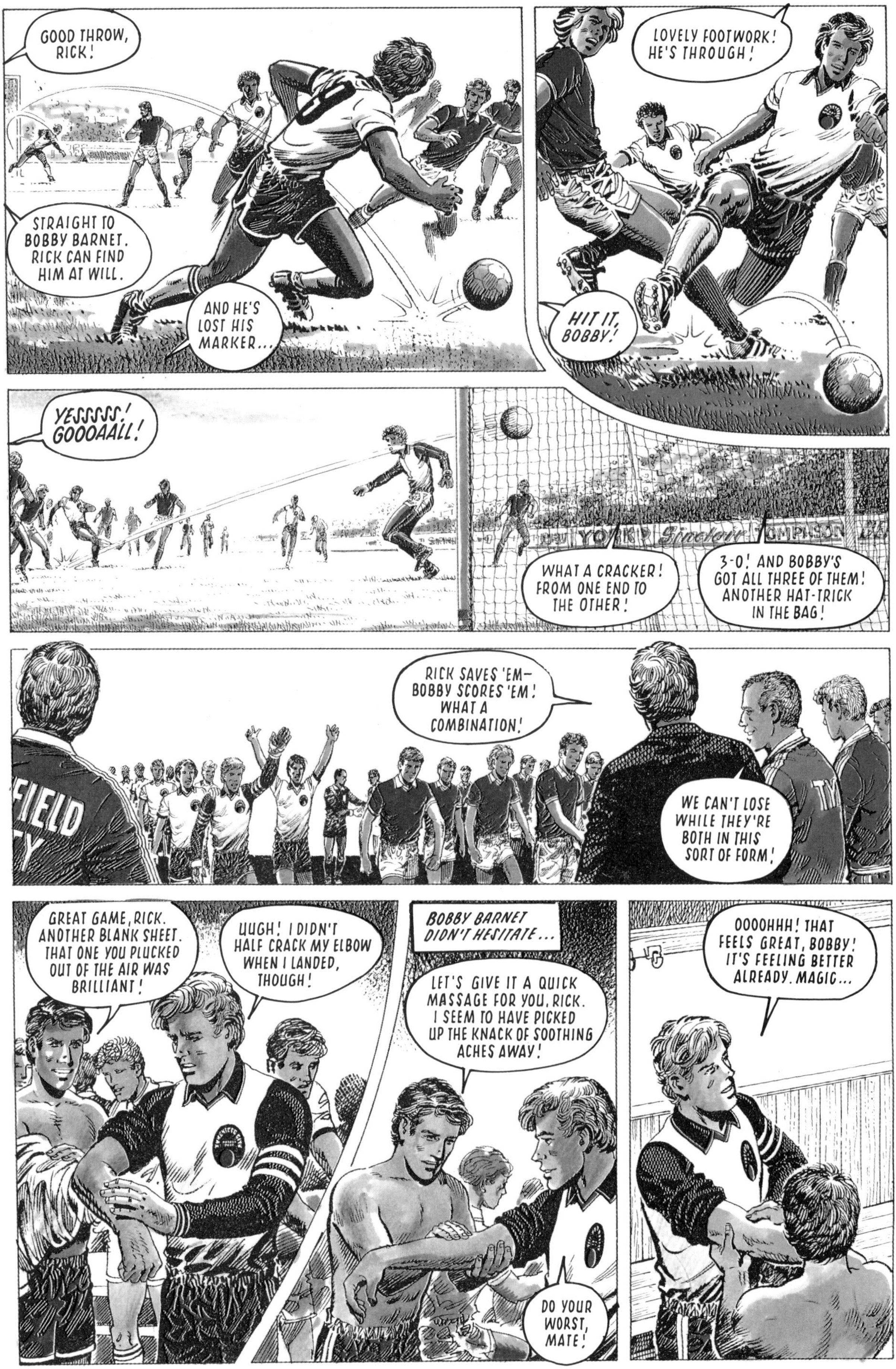

GOOD THROW, RICK!
STRAIGHT TO BOBBY BARNET. RICK CAN FIND HIM AT WILL.
AND HE'S LOST HIS MARKER...
LOVELY FOOTWORK! HE'S THROUGH!
HIT IT, BOBBY!
YESSSSS! GOOOAALL!
WHAT A CRACKER! FROM ONE END TO THE OTHER!
3-0! AND BOBBY'S GOT ALL THREE OF THEM! ANOTHER HAT-TRICK IN THE BAG!

THANKS! AT LEAST I'LL BE 100% TO FACE BLACKSTONE ATHLETIC NEXT SATURDAY NOW...
BLACKSTONE...THE MOST PHYSICAL SIDE IN THE LEAGUE, THEY'RE ALWAYS DIFFICULT TO PLAY AGAINST.

DON'T YOU WORRY, RICK. TOUGH TEAM OR NOT, WE'LL BURY 'EM!
YOU'RE ON, BOBBY. YOU SCORE 'EM, I'LL STOP 'EM. THAT SHOULD BE ENOUGH.

BUT BLACKSTONE HAD A NEW, UNCOMPROMISING COACH...
NO MESSING ABOUT TODAY, LADS! THEIR STRIKER, BOBBY BARNET, IS LETHAL NEAR GOAL...
...SO I WANT HIM TAKEN OUT, OKAY?

YOU HEARD ME. WHAT DID I SAY?
TAKE HIM OUT!

RIGHT. DO IT–OR DON'T BOTHER COMING BACK IN HERE AFTERWARDS! TYNEFIELD ARE THE LEAGUE LEADERS AND WE'RE GONNA SLAUGHTER 'EM!

IT'S FUNNY, BOBBY, BUT I'M NOT REALLY LOOKING FORWARD TO THIS GAME. I DON'T KNOW WHY...
YOU SHOULDN'T BE WORRYING, RICK. YOU STOP EVERYTHING THAT COMES YOUR WAY...THAT'S WHY WE'RE TOP OF THE LEAGUE!

PHEEP!!

PHEW! I KNOW BLACKSTONE ARE WELL-KNOWN FOR IT, BUT THEY'RE REALLY AGGRESSIVE TODAY!
DISHING IT OUT! POOR OLD TYNEFIELD.
MUST BE THEIR NEW COACH.

YAAAAAH!
AND BOBBY BARNET IS GETTING MORE THAN HIS FAIR SHARE OF STICK!

NOW LISTEN. I DON'T LIKE THAT SORT OF FOUL. PLEASE BE MORE CAREFUL...
AND THE REF'S A REAL WIMP. WITHOUT STRONG CONTROL, THIS COULD GO FROM BAD TO WORSE FOR TYNEFIELD...

EVEN RICK CAME UNDER PRESSURE...
AAAAHHHH!
FOUL! YOU CAN'T KNOCK THE GOALKEEPER WHEN HIS FEET ARE OFF THE GROUND!

A SHORT KICK OUT OF THE AREA, A PUSH BACK, AND RICK WAS ABLE TO KICK IT LONG...
BOBBY!
HE'S UNMARKED!
BUT THE BLACKSTONE DEFENCE HAD BEEN WELL BRIEFED...
THE BLACKSTONE DEFENDER'S COMING IN LIKE A TRAIN!
WATCH OUT, BOBBY...

AAAARRRGGGHHH!
THE SICKENING CRACK COULD BE HEARD FROM RICK'S GOAL...
OH, NO! BOBBY! THAT EVIL TACKLE...
TAKE IT EASY, BOBBY. YOU'LL BE OKAY...
UUUUHHH! THANKS, RICK...
AT LEAST THE REF'S DONE THE RIGHT THING. SENT HIM OFF. BUT THAT DOESN'T HELP BOBBY. HIS LEG IS DEFINITELY BROKEN...
NEXT DAY...
I WANT YOU TO BE THE FIRST TO SIGN MY PLASTER, RICK...
IT'S A DEAL, BOBBY. AND TO BE DIFFERENT, I'LL DO IT LEFT-HANDED...
NOT BAD, EH? AT LEAST YOU CAN READ IT!
Rick Stewa

LISTEN, BOBBY. THE YOUTH TEAM DON'T HAVE A PHYSIO AT PRESENT. WHAT ABOUT TAKING OVER? YOU'RE A NATURAL...

ME, RICK? I COULDN'T-!

YOU COULD!

AND TYNEFIELD'S NEXT OPPONENTS—IN A YOUTH CUP MATCH—WERE BLACKSTONE ATHLETIC!

OH, GREAT, RICK! WHAT A START FOR ME AS A LEARNER-PHYSIO!

COME ON, BOBBY. NOTHING LIKE A TOUGH TEST TO START OFF WITH! YOU'LL HANDLE IT!

WHAT IS IT, JASON? ANKLE..?

YES, BOBBY...

IT WAS ONE OF THOSE DAYS THAT RICK COULD DO NOTHING WRONG...

A SUPER SAVE!

GREAT STOP! RICK'S KEEPING CITY IN THE GAME!

FANTASTIC! HE'S THE BEST!

BUT THEN...
AAAAHHHHHH!
A LATE TACKLE ON THE GOALIE!
THAT WAS EVIL, BLACKSTONE!
BRING ON THE PHYSIO!
AAAAAAH, THAT FEELS GREAT, BOBBY! YOU HAD MAGIC FEET, BUT DID ANYONE EVER TELL YOU YOU HAD MAGIC HANDS?
THANKS, RICK!
YOU KNOW SOMETHING, RICK? I'M FINDING THIS PHYSIO BUSINESS NEARLY AS SATISFYING AS GOALSCORING!
SO MY DAD'S DIARY CAME GOOD AGAIN. A PHYSIO IS WORTH HIS WEIGHT IN GOLD...
... AND THE BEAUTY OF IT WAS: WE FINALLY BEAT BLACKSTONE ATHLETIC IN THE CUP IN INJURY TIME! SERVED THEM RIGHT!
The End

ROCKY'S

LESSON

Roy Race's son was a player of considerable potential, but first he had to learn a few things ...

Roy Race was having an afternoon off. For once, the world-famous player-manager of First Division Melchester Rovers was standing on the touchline and not on the pitch. He'd come to see his son Roy, or "Rocky", play in the semi-final of the Juveniles' Cup against Clifton Valley Colts.

In recent months, Roy junior had begun to show all the superb footballing skills of his internationally-known father. Speed on and off the ball; an ability to build dangerous attacking moves from midfield; intelligent use of the open space; and last but not least, a powerful shot with either foot.

Now the semi-final match was drawing to a close. It had been a hard, fast-moving game and the scores were level at one goal each with only ten minutes to go. Roy was standing with Melchester youth team manager Danny Trent. "The game can still go either way," he said. "What we need is a last-minute, all-out effort to grab that winning goal."

A long, solo run by the Melchester winger took the opposing defence by surprise. From the corner flag, the ball came curving back hard and low towards the edge of the penalty box. Rocky and a Clifton Valley

Rocky looked pleased with himself when he arrived home. "The photo session was fine, Dad," he said.

defender went for it together, and it was young Roy who came out of the tackle with the ball at his feet. He waltzed past another defender and cut inside. Ten metres away, a Melchester striker was running into space in front of goal and screaming for the pass. Instead, Rocky changed direction, side-stepped to the left and shot, a high, curving ball that slid under the bar and into the back of the net from an acute and apparently impossible angle.

Rocky had done it again! Melchester Youth were through to the final of the Juveniles' Cup!

Grinning from ear to ear he faced his father.

"Not bad for a little 'un, eh, Dad?"

Roy nodded. "Great game, son, but you were a shade lucky with that winning goal. Pete Stockley was in a far better scoring position. You should have passed."

"I thought he was offside," said Rocky a trifle crossly. "Anyway, it went in, that's the main thing."

"I still say you had more luck than you deserved. Always remember that football is a team game."

"I don't think you're giving your son the credit he deserves, Mr Race. That winning goal was a touch of pure magic."

Roy turned to find himself facing a tall, pale-faced young man with bobbing fair hair and thin lips. "I'm Max Thornton," he said, "freelance reporter and photographer. Your son has been opening a few eyes in recent weeks, I'd like to do a photo-story on him."

"At least give the lad time to have his bath!"

"That's all right, Dad, now or later it's all the same to me. What do you want to know, Mr Thornton?"

"Oh, the usual kind of things. What it's like to be the famous son of a famous father....what your plans are for the future...."

"The first thing I'm planning to do is win the Juveniles' Cup," grinned Rocky. "After that I'm hoping to be promoted to the Melchester first-team squad. I intend to be just as famous as my Dad...."

As the boy and Max Thornton walked towards the pavilion, deep in conversation, Danny Trent turned to Roy Race senior. "Your son's certainly gaining in confidence these days," he said. "To hear him talk, you'd think he was a full-time pro already."

"Exactly! And it's worrying me, Danny. There's been a subtle change in young Roy's attitude for some time now. Like that goal he scored today. It was a beaut, all right, but he should have passed to Pete Stockley."

"What are you trying to say, Roy?"

"That the kid's getting too over-confident for his own good!"

There was worse to come on the following Saturday night after Melchester Rovers' home game against Walham City. It was a match that Roy and his players certainly wanted to forget in a hurry. Nothing would go right. It was a wet and windy afternoon and from the very first whistle, every move that Rovers made seemed destined to go wrong.

In the dying minutes, a Walham forward hammered the ball into the back of the net for the only goal of the match.

That night when Roy got home, he found Rocky shaking his head dolefully. Penny, Roy's wife, was there too.

"Walham City are third from the bottom of the First Division, Dad," said Roy junior. "Losing one-nil to that bunch is a pretty miserable result."

"You don't have to remind me," said Roy sharply. "It's a game I'd rather forget."

"If you want my advice, I reckon you should have some new young blood in the first team squad."

Roy felt a hot flush of rage turning his face red. "Listen to me, boy," he said sharply. "If and when I ever want your advice, I'll ask for it."

"All right then, if that's the way you want it...." With an angry toss of his head, Rocky stormed out of the room.

"Bit hard on him, weren't you?" said Penny quietly.

"No I wasn't! Ever since his winning streak with the youth team, that kid's been getting too big for his boots."

"It's only a phase he's going through, Roy."

"I flaming well hope so....and the sooner the better!"

The final of the Western Region Juveniles' Cup was due to be played midweek, on the following Wednesday. On the Tuesday evening before the match, Rocky came downstairs carrying a black holdall. About to have their tea, Penny and Roy looked up in surprise.

"Sorry, Mum, got to go out for an hour or so. Max Thornton wants to see me for another photo session."

"More super-star material, I suppose," said Roy sourly.

Roy junior flushed. "Mr Thornton is interested in the Melchester Youth Team, that's all. He reckons it's the best one the city's ever had. He reckons I'm pretty good, too!"

Seconds later the dishes rattled violently on the kitchen table as Rocky stormed out and slammed the front door behind him.

"You've done it again, Roy," said Penny ruefully.

"Maybe I have, but all this so-called big-deal publicity is turning the boy's head."

The youngster returned just over an hour and a half later. "How did the photo session go?" asked Roy casually.

"Fine, Dad, just fine," said his son with a secretive smile. "In fact it couldn't have been better. I'll grab something to eat, then have an early night for the big match tomorrow."

As the boy closed the door behind him, Roy looked up and frowned. "Penny, have you changed your perfume, or something? There's a funny smell in here!"

"Very romantic, Mr Race....I don't think!"

"Sorry, I didn't mean it like that, but there is a strange scent in here!"

Penny sniffed hard. "Yes, you're right. I did buy a new brand of ecological air freshener for the kitchen the other day. Maybe it's that."

The day of the Juveniles' Cup Final dawned bright and clear.

Melchester Youth Team manager Danny Trent was in a confident mood as he ushered his players into the dressing-room. The other finalists were Burndale Juniors, tough, capable, and with several promising players in their side. But their style of play was predictable, and they lacked individualists like Rocky and Pete Stockley.

As the teams trotted out for their pre-match warm-up, Roy saw Rocky dart behind one of the

goals and speak quickly to two men who were standing there. One was Max Thornton, the other a fat, sweaty individual wearing a loud sports jacket.

"Who's that guy with Max Thornton?" Roy asked Danny Trent.

"A fellow called Harry Hopkins. He's a wholesaler wheeler and dealer in cheap sportswear and equipment."

"Then I wonder what his connection is with Max Thornton.... and my son," said Roy grimly.

But if Danny Trent had had high hopes of the Melchester lads scoring an early goal, those hopes were dashed within the opening minutes. From the first blast of the whistle it was Burndale Juniors who were off their marks like greyhounds unleashed; hunting every ball, tackling with fierce determination and forcing Melchester back in a sustained wave of attacks. The defence just couldn't hold out! Burndale forced a corner and their striker's blond head rose elegantly to head the ball into the back of the net. Burndale Juniors 1, Melchester Youth 0.

Danny Trent screamed instructions to his players without success. Time and again he urged Rocky and Pete Stockley to build up attacking moves and get back into the game. Although young Stockley was playing his heart out and putting a hundred per cent effort into everything he did, it was Roy Race's son who was letting the side down.He was a shadow of his former self: slow off the mark, tackling weakly and passing with about as much accuracy as a five-year-old playing ball in a public park. "This is more than big-match nerves, " said Roy senior angrily. "Something's wrong"

Just before half-time, Burndale scored again, and Rocky Race was close to tears as he walked slowly into the dressing-room to be met by his father and Danny Trent. "Okay, son....tell me all about it," said Roy gently.

"I-I should have shown you this morning, Dad....but I couldn't. I just couldn't! I hoped it might go away before match-time." The boy had sat down, untied his boots, taken them off, and was now stripping his socks off too. From the tops of his thighs to his toes, Rocky's legs were covered in a bright-red rash.

"What the heck caused this?" asked Roy.

Rocky reached under a towel on the bench behind him, took out a large jar of ointment. On the label was written:

HOPKINS' HYDROGEN BALM....REVITALISES AND SOOTHES ACHING MUSCLES.

Roy unscrewed the lid and sniffed the sludge-like paste inside.

"This is the stuff I smelt in the lounge last night. No doubt you tried it out during your photo session with Max Thornton, right?"

Rocky nodded miserably.

"Yes. When I arrived at Max's studio a man called Harry Hopkins was there too. He said he was trying to market a new muscle ointment and would I like to try a free sample. He said if it was successful I might even get a fee for helping to sell it."

"What a flaming rip-off," said Roy furiously. "First Thornton butters the kid up with all the super-star stuff, then along comes Hopkins with a cheap embrocation and an eye for free publicity. I can see all the adverts now: 'AS USED BY THE SON OF ROY RACE! EXCLUSIVE OFFER, BUY NOW!' Those crooks could easily have made a fortune out of this rubbish!"

"I can't play in the second half, Dad," said Rocky miserably. "You'll have to substitute me."

"Not yet! Get into the shower now and wash that balm muck off your legs. Then we'll spray a calomine lotion on them and give you clean socks. With any luck the rash will die down."

Roy's desperate half-time remedy worked within fifteen minutes of its application, and from that time on, Melchester Youth fought their way back into the game with ever-increasing determination. With half an hour to go, Rocky broke clear on the right. He pounded to the corner flag and squared the ball low and hard for Pete Stockley on the edge of the box. The striker hit the ball on the run, a fierce, twisting shot that streaked high into the right-hand corner of the net.

It was Pete Stockley too, who snatched the equaliser eight minutes later. A bad clearance by a defender was sliced acutely across the face of the goal, and Pete hit the bouncing ball on the half-volley, a hammer-blow of a shot that streaked into the net with the 'keeper flat-footed.

From that moment on, Burndale went to pieces. Against the speed and inspiration of Melchester's play they could do nothing. They packed their defence and tried to hang on, but it was not to be. With three minutes left, Rocky Race picked up a wide Burndale clearance on the halfway line and bored his way forward.

Then Rocky saw Pete Stockley out of the corner of his eye. Roy junior didn't hesitate. He squared the ball sideways and seconds later it was bulging the back of the net. Pete Stockley had scored a hat-trick and Melchester Youth had won the Juveniles' Cup by three goals to two!

Roy Race was the first to congratulate his son as the two teams trooped off to thunderous cheers. "You handed Stockley that last goal on a plate," he said.

"Pete was in a better position than I was to score the winner," said Rocky quietly. "I think I've learned what teamwork is all about at last! I'll never be as good as you are, Dad, that's for sure." Then Rocky paused, looked up and said with a grin..."Well, not for a few years yet, anyway!"

"Ha, ha, ha, nice one, son! Now let's go and find a certain Max Thornton and Harry Hopkins. I reckon we both have a few things to say to that pair!"

"Okay....but you can do the talking, Dad. I'll just explode a hydrogen balm under them!"

NIGEL CLOUGH
(Nottingham Forest)

Both Nigel Clough and his father Brian have worn the No.9 shirt with great distinction for England and their respective clubs, but there the similarity ends. Whereas Brian was a powerful, traditional, record-breaking goalscorer, Nigel plays a deeper role quite content to create space, and changes, for his fellow strikers.

Nigel has played a big part in Forest's recent successes, notably in cup football. They won the Littlewoods Cup in 1989 and 1990, the Simod Cup in 1989 and were Runners-up in the 1991 FA Cup. He was first capped in 1989, against Chile, by Bobby Robson and with new manager Graham Taylor looking to impose his own style on the England team, Nigel can expect to win many more caps.

No doubt his father, and Forest boss, Brian Clough will be looking on approvingly!

ASK ME ANOTHER!

Put yourself on the spot and test your soccer knowledge.

1 Who am I? I started my league career at Crewe, went to play for Vancouver in Canada, before joining Liverpool as their keeper.
ANSWER:

2 Which player has NOT played for England?
TONY ADAMS DES WALKER
MARK WRIGHT ERIC YOUNG
ANSWER:

3 Who do you support if you watch The Seasiders at Bloomfield Road?
ANSWER:

4 Start at the letter top left of the box of letters and move one letter at a time to spell out the names of TWO soccer sides. You can go in any direction except diagonally.

C	**O**	**S**	**O**
E	**V**	**Y**	**U**
N	**T**	**R**	**T**
D	**N**	**E**	**H**

ANSWER:

5 What is the colour that links all these teams?
ABERDEEN LIVERPOOL
MAN UTD MIDDLESBROUGH
ANSWER:

6 Rearrange the letters to spell out the name of a soccer boss.
YEKNN GILDAHLS
ANSWER:

7 Which TWO clubs have DAVE BEASANT, VINNY JONES and DENNIS WISE played for in the same side?
ANSWER:

8 Peter Shreeves has had two spells as manager of which London club?
ANSWER:

9 Which club has Graeme Souness NOT played for?
ABERDEEN
LIVERPOOL
RANGERS
ANSWER:

10 Which teams are playing when The Eagles take on The Gunners?
ANSWER:

11 Rearrange the letters to spell out the name of a top class England striker.
NALA ERASHER
ANSWER:

12 Who was appointed manager of Oldham Athletic way back in July 1982?
ANSWER:

13 Peter Beardsley, Gary Ablett and Steve McMahon have all played for the same TWO North West teams. Which teams?
ANSWER:

14 Which of these teams is NOT a City?
BRADFORD COVENTRY
DERBY STOKE
ANSWER:

15 Peter Shilton seems to have been playing for ever. When do you think he made his League debut: 1965/66, 1970/71 or 1973/74?
ANSWER:

16 Match up the parts of the names to form FOUR soccer sides. Which piece is NOT needed?

FUL	**TER**	**TIC**
DON	**MILL**	**WALL**
HAM	**SWIN**	**CEL**

ANSWER:

17 JOHN BYRNE, COLIN CLARKE and ROY WEGERLE have all been strikers with which London club?
ANSWER:

18 Who am I? I'm an Eire international midfielder. I started with Southampton, moved to Norwich then on to Chelsea.
ANSWER:

19 Rearrange the letters to make the name of a First Division ground.
AMBER LANLAL (Two words)
ANSWER:

20 Who was top scorer for Arsenal in season 88/89, 89/90, and 90/91?
ANSWER:

ANSWERS: 1 Bruce Grobbelaar, 2 Eric Young, 3 Blackpool, 4 Coventry, Southend, 5 Red, 6 Kenny Dalglish, 7 Wimbledon and Chelsea, 8 Spurs, 9 Aberdeen, 10 Crystal Palace and Arsenal, 11 Alan Shearer, 12 Joe Royle, 13 Liverpool and Everton, 14 Derby, 15 1965/66, 16 TER. (Fulham, Celtic, Swindon, Millwall), 17 QPR, 18 Andy Townsend, 19 Bramall Lane, 20 Alan Smith.

ASK ME ANOTHER!

1 Mel Sterland, Chris Fairclough and David Batty have all played together for which club?
ANSWER:

2 True or false? Dundee have a keeper called DAN DEE?
ANSWER:

3 If you are at Goodison Park watching The Dons which teams are you watching?
ANSWER:

4 Which of these teams has NOT been managed by Ron Atkinson?
ASTON VILLA   LUTON
MAN. UTD   SHEFF. WEDS.
ANSWER:

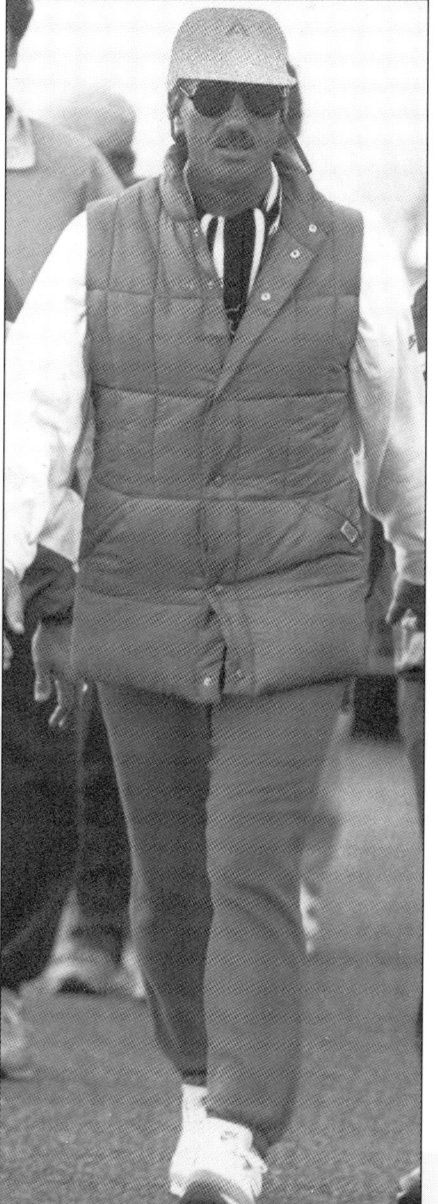

5 Look at the sentence below then try to find a hidden team name by joining words, or parts of words together.
HE WAS TO KEEP A CLEAN SHEET THAT GAME
ANSWER:

6 What name links Mark of Liverpool, Ian of Arsenal and Tommy of Leicester?
ANSWER:

7 Rearrange the letters to name the international keeper.
GRAND MAYO
ANSWER:

8 What word is in the ground names of the following teams?
BLACKBURN   OLDHAM
SUNDERLAND   WEST HAM
ANSWER:

9 True or false? Ian Botham has been a player at Scunthorpe.
ANSWER:

10 Take just one letter from each word to spell out the name of a striker called John.
FIT CAN USE HIM
AIM END PUT
ANSWER:

11 Which of these teams has DEAN SAUNDERS not played for?
BRIGHTON   DERBY   IPSWICH
LIVERPOOL   OXFORD
ANSWER:

12 Who am I? I started as a 16 year old with Birmingham. After playing for Forest, Man City, Sampdoria and Rangers, I became player manager of QPR and then Sheff. Weds.
ANSWER:

13 What's the colour that links these teams?
DERBY   LEEDS   SPURS
ANSWER:

14 STEVE BRUCE, ANDY LINIGHAN and DALE GORDON have all played for this club. Is it ASTON VILLA, NORWICH or NOTTM FOREST?
ANSWER:

15 What's the surname shared between Gary of Aston Villa and Paul of Manchester United?
ANSWER:

16 Strikergram! Rearrange the letters to spell out a Scottish striker.
HERON JOB SNORT (2 words)
ANSWER:

17 What position do NIGEL SPINK, BRYAN GUNN and STEVE SUTTON all play in?
ANSWER:

18 Which club had GARY PALLISTER and TONY MOWBRAY as a formidable pair of centre backs? Was it CELTIC, MIDDLESBROUGH or NEWCASTLE?
ANSWER:

19 Rearrange each line of letters to spell out a player's last name. You'll find that reading in a diagonal from top left to bottom right another name is formed.

M O Y B L _ _ _ _ _
T B T Y A _ _ _ _ _
N O R M A _ _ _ _ _
W A H S L _ _ _ _ _
T H H A E _ _ _ _ _

ANSWER:

20 Which team did Graham Taylor manage directly before he took on the England job?
ANSWER:

ANSWERS:
1 Leeds, 2 False, 3 Everton v Wimbledon, 4 Luton, 5 Stoke, 6 Wright, 7 Andy Goram, 8 Park, 9 True, 10 Fashanu, 11 Ipswich, 12 Trevor Francis, 13 White, 14 Norwich, 15 Parker, 16 John Robertson, 17 Keeper, 18 Middlesbrough, 19 Molby, Batty, Moran, Walsh, Heath, MARSH. 20 Aston Villa.

ASK ME ANOTHER!

1 MARK WALTERS, CHRIS WOODS and TERRY HURLOCK have all played for which club?
ANSWER:

2 Groundgram! Can you rearrange the letters to name a famous London stadium? (Three words)
ANSWER:

3 Which teams are involved if The Blades visit Highbury?
ANSWER:

4 Who am I? I'm a left back for Forest and England. I knocked in 11 League in the 91-92 season.
ANSWER:

5 Which team does NOT play in stripes?
GRIMSBY NORWICH SHEFF WEDS SUNDERLAND
ANSWER:

6 **SEOUVETHRATLOLN** The name of a team and their keeper are mixed together. Can you sort them out?
ANSWER:

7 What's the first name shared by McAllister and SPEED of Leeds?
ANSWER:

8 **JIMMY ADAMSON DON REVIE ALF RAMSEY BOBBY ROBSON They have all managed which soccer team?**
ANSWER:

9 Start at the letter top left of the box of letters and move one letter at a time to spell out the names of TWO soccer sides. You can go in any direction except diagonally.

B A R N
N E L S
O Y B R
T H G I

ANSWER:

10 What's the shared name with these clubs?
CAMBRIDGE ROTHERHAM WEST HAM
ANSWER:

11 He scored on his debuts for Portsmouth, Nottm Forest and Man United. Can you name this England midfielder?
ANSWER:

12 Which country hosted the 1992 European Championship?
ANSWER:

13 One of the great F.A. Cup shocks happened when Arsenal - the reigning League champions - were knocked out of the F.A. Cup Third Round in January '92. Their opponents were near the bottom of Division Four. Were they LINCOLN, ROCHDALE or WREXHAM?
ANSWER:

14 Rearrange the letters to make the name of a young Welsh star.
GARY GINGS
ANSWER:

15 Who has NOT been the boss of Newcastle?
OSSIE ARDILES JACK CHARLTON KEVIN KEEGAN HOWARD WILKINSON
ANSWER:

16 True or false? Brian Clough was once linked with the job of Welsh team manager.
ANSWER:

17 Against which country did Gary Lineker score his first goal for England?
ANSWER:

18 Use TWO different letters of the alphabet to finish off the name of this midfield star.
_ R _ VOR S _ _ V _ N
ANSWER:

19 Arbroath gave Bon Accord the biggest hammering in this country's senior soccer. Was the score: Was the score: 15 – 0, 25 – 3 or 36 – 0?
ANSWER:

20 Argentina were the beaten finalists in the last World Cup. Who won the trophy?
ANSWER:

ANSWERS: 1 Rangers, 2 White Hart Lane, 3 Arsenal v Sheff Utd, 4 Stuart Pearce, 5 Norwich, 6 Southall, Everton, 7 Gary, 8 England, 9 Barnsley, Brighton, 10 United, 11 Neil Webb, 12 Sweden, 13 Wrexham, 14 Ryan Giggs, 15 Howard Wilkinson, 16 True, 17 Eire, 18 Trevor Steven, 19 36 – 0, 20 West Germany.

ASK ME ANOTHER!

1 What name is shared by Arsenal players Hillier and Seaman?
ANSWER:

2 Which two teams are playing when The Owls visit Loftus Road?
ANSWER:

3 What position do Rob Jones and Lee Dixon play?
ANSWER:

4 True or false? IAN RUSH has spent all his career with Liverpool.
ANSWER:

5 What are the colourful last names of Man City's DAVID and Luton and Forest's KINGSLEY?
ANSWER:

6 Who am I? I'm an England striker known for my heading ability. I've played for Coventry and Portsmouth, gone abroard then moved north of the border with Glasgow Rangers.
ANSWER:

7 **O ARROW CARD**
Rearrange the letters to make a soccer ground. (Two words)
ANSWER:

8 What's the colour link between CELTIC, HIBS and PLYMOUTH?
ANSWER:

9 Colin Harvey took over at Everton from Howard Kendall. Who in turn took over from Colin Harvey?
ANSWER:

10 True or false? Keeper Les Sealey was on loan with Manchester United when he was called up for the replay of an F.A. Cup Final.
ANSWER:

11 Start at the letter top left of the box of letters and move one letter at a time to spell out the names of TWO soccer sides. You can go in any direction except diagonally.

A Y V O
B R E C
E T N N
R D E E

ANSWER:

12 LAWRIE McMENEMY, CHRIS NICHOLL and IAN BRANFOOT have all been the manager with which South Coast club?
ANSWER:

13 BRIAN'S son is NIGEL. ARCHIE's son is SCOTT. Both lads play and both dads are part of the management and training set up at Forest. Can you supply the surnames?
ANSWER:

14 Rearrange the letters to make the name of a Welsh striker.
HUGH MAKERS
ANSWER:

15 Veteran Ray Wilkins has been playing as well as ever. When did he make his League debut? Was it 1973-74, 77-78 or 84-85?
ANSWER:

16 PAUL ELLIOTT and TONY CASCARINO have played for the same three clubs. ASTON VILLA and CHELSEA are two of them. Can you name the third?
ANSWER:

17 What's the first name of Fenwick and Venables of Spurs?
ANSWER:

18 Is it necessary to be shown a yellow card before a player can be shown a red one?
ANSWER:

19 Who plays at Filbert Street: DERBY, LEICESTER, WBA?
ANSWER:

20 Which country hosted the 1990 World Cup? Was it BELGIUM, ITALY or SPAIN?
ANSWER:

ANSWERS:
1 David, 2 QPR v Sheff Weds, 3 Right back, 4 False, 5 White, Black, 6 Mark Hateley, 7 Carrow Road, 8 Green, 9 Howard Kendall, 10 True, 11 Aberdeen, Coventry, 12 Southampton, 13 Clough, Gemmill, 14 Mark Hughes, 15 1973-74, 16 Celtic, 17 Terry, 18 No, 19 Leicester, 20 Italy.

ASK ME ANOTHER!

1 **LLEUKEIDCS**
The name of a team and their keeper have got mixed up. Can you sort them out?
ANSWER:

2 Who am I? I've played for both Rangers and Celtic, as well as with Watford and Everton. I'm a Scottish striker.
ANSWER:

3 What's the name that links MEADOWBANK and PARTICK?
ANSWER:

4 PETER WITHE, BOBBY GOULD and DAVE BASSETT have all been managers with which club?
ANSWER:

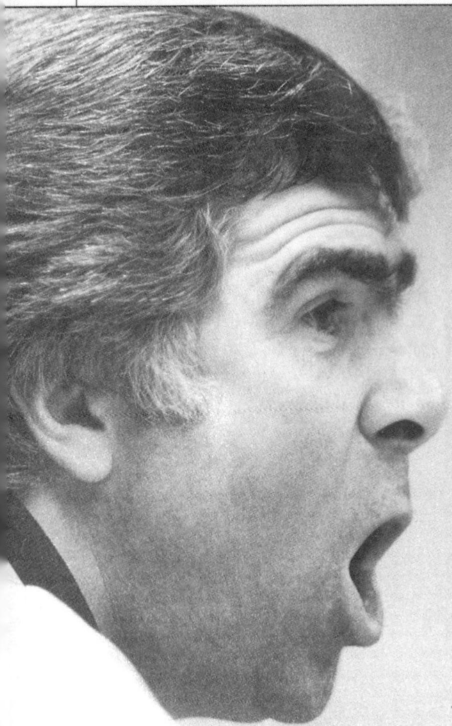

5 True or false? John Wark has been signed by Ipswich on three occasions.
ANSWER:

6 Which country does David Hirst play for?
ANSWER:

7 If The Hammers are visiting The County Ground which teams are playing?
ANSWER:

8 David Pleat has had two spells as manager with this club, nicknamed The Hatters. Can you name the team?
ANSWER:

9 Terry Yorath manages which country?
ANSWER:

10 **ROUGH ILL HOBS**
Rearrange the letters to make the name of a Yorkshire soccer ground. (One word)
ANSWER:

11 What's the first name shared by Man Utd's MARTIN and SHARPE?
ANSWER:

12 In soccer a CANARY is a FOX. Can you explain this?
ANSWER:

13 What's the colour link between ASTON VILLA and BURNLEY?
ANSWER:

14 Which country does Jan Molby play for?
ANSWER:

15 Start at the letter top left of the box of letters and move one letter at a time to spell out the names of TWO soccer sides. You can go in any direction except diagonally.

C N P L
H O M Y
A T O H
R L U T

ANSWER:

16 Which club have VIV ANDERSON, NIGEL JEMSON and STEVE HODGE played for?
ANSWER:

17 In an F.A. Cup Final who plays for both sides? (Yes, it's a trick question!)
ANSWER:

18 **SANDRA MELRIP**
Rearrange the letters to make the name of an Arsenal star.
ANSWER:

19 What do the letters A.E.T. mean when they appear by the result of a game?
ANSWER:

20 **DEEP_ _ _ _GORDON**
What word will fill the spaces, ending the name of a ground, and starting off the name of a player?
ANSWER:

ANSWERS:
1. Lukic, Leeds, 2 Mo Johnstone, 3 Thistle, 4 Wimbledon, 5 True, 6 England, 7 Notts County v West Ham, 8 Luton, 9 Wales, 10 Hillsborough, 11 Lee, 12 Ruel Fox plays for Norwich, The Canaries, 13 Claret, 14 Denmark, 15 Charlton, Plymouth, 16 Nottm Forest, 17 The band, 18 Anders Limpar, 19 After Extra Time, 20 Dale, Deepdale, Dale Gordon.

ASK ME ANOTHER!

1 He was playing for Chelsea against one of his old clubs, Sheffield United, in an F.A. Cup Fifth Round tie and managed to get booked in the first minute. Who is he?
ANSWER:

2 Bryan Robson had a long and distinguished career with England. Did he manage to win 100 caps?
ANSWER:

3 **CHARLTON FORFAR OLDHAM** What name links these clubs?
ANSWER:

4 KEVIN RICHARDSON, JOHN ALDRIDGE and DALIAN ATKINSON have all played soccer in Spain with the same club. Was it: **REAL MADRID, REAL SOCIEDAD** or **REAL ESTATE**?
ANSWER:

5 Who am I? I'm an Eire international defender and I've played more League games than anyone for Arsenal.
ANSWER:

6 **FSOLUTOHAWMPETROSN** The names of a team, and their keeper have got mixed up. Can you sort them out?
ANSWER:

7 Gazza injured himself during the 1991 F.A. Cup Final. But who was the player on the receiving end of his last lunging tackle? Was it **NIGEL CLOUGH, GARY CHARLES** or **STUART PEARCE**?
ANSWER:

8 Which player has NOT played for Liverpool?
JIMMY CARTER NIGEL SPACKMAN GORDON STRACHAN STEVE STAUNTON
ANSWER:

9 Start at the top left of the box of letters and move one letter at a time to spell out the names of FOUR soccer sides. You can go in any direction except diagonally.

S K E R E
T O W B D
A G I Y N
N L U T O

ANSWER:

10 True or false? Peter Beardsley was released by Manchester United without playing a game for them.
ANSWER:

11 Which Scottish soccer side plays home games at Rugby Park? Is it **HIBERNIAN, KILMARNOCK** or **MONTROSE**?
ANSWER:

12 Which country will host the 1994 World Cup?
ANSWER:

13 Which teams are involved in the scrap when The Foxes take on The Magpies?
ANSWER:

14 **CHAIN REACH SO ILL** Rearrange the letters to make the name of an experienced Scottish striker.
ANSWER:

15 What colour links **MEADOWBANK, MOTHERWELL** and **BRADFORD**?
ANSWER:

16 What's the shared first name of Liverpool's Nicol and McManaman?
ANSWER:

17 **LEICESTER, EVERTON, BARCELONA, SPURS.** Who is the super striker that links those clubs together?
ANSWER:

18 **RIP RED TEE** Rearrange the letters to make the name of a player/manager.
ANSWER:

19 Which club could once boast that its record fee received was £1,000,000 for the sale of Mike Milligan to Everton in August 1990, and its record fee paid was £600,000 to Everton for Mike Milligan in June 1991?
ANSWER:

20 Who is playing in a local derby if The Terrors visit Dens Park?
ANSWER:

ANSWERS: 1 Vinny Jones, 2 No, 3 Athletic, 4 Real Sociedad, 5 David O'Leary, 6 Flowers, Southampton, 7 Gary Charles, 8 Gordon Strachan, 9 Stoke, Wigan, Luton, Derby, 10 True, 11 Kilmarnock, 12 USA, 13 Leicester (Foxes), Newcastle (Magpies), 14 Charlie Nicholas, 15 Amber, 16 Steve, 17 Gary Lineker, 18 Peter Reid, 19 Oldham, 20 Dundee at home to Dundee Utd.

FOOTBALLING

Soccer runs in the family! A brief look at players with the same name...

When Danny, Ray and Rodney Wallace played for Southampton against Sheffield Wednesday on October 22nd, 1988 it was the first time since 1919/20 that three brothers had played together in a First Division side.

On that occasion John, George and William Carr turned out for Middlesbrough.

Many brothers have played together but not more than three. However, when Notts County played Nottingham Forest in the F.A. Cup in 1978, County had TWO sets of three brothers...the Curshams and the Greenhalghs. We bet Brian Moore is glad he didn't have to commentate on THAT game!

Perhaps the most famous brothers in boots are Bobby and Jack Charlton who helped England win the World Cup in 1966.

They first played together against Scotland in 1965 and they were the first to represent their country in the same match since Fred and Frank Forman in 1899.

The Formans are unique in being the only brothers to play in the same

club (Nottingham Forest) and international team.

There have been instances of brothers playing for different countries. John Hollins, the former Chelsea manager, played for England while brother Dave was Wales's goalkeeper. John was born in Guildford, Dave in Bangor.

When Wales played Northern Ireland there were two sets of Welsh brothers - John and Mel Charles and Ivor and Len Allchurch.

There have been many sons following in their father's footsteps - Nigel Clough of Forest, where dad Brian is manager is the most famous in recent years - but only once have father and son played in the same League team.

That was in May, 1951, when Alec Herd and his son David played for

Rodney (top left), Ray (left) and Danny Wallace (above). Pointing the finger is John Hollins.

FAMILIES!

Stockport in a Third Division (North) game against Hartlepool.

The most prolific soccer family is the Allens. Cousins Clive (Chelsea), Paul (Spurs) and Martin (West Ham) are currently League stars, while Clive's dad Les played for Spurs and Chelsea as well as managing QPR. Another Allen, Bradley, is breaking through at QPR.

Twins Ron and Paul Futcher moved from Chester to Luton together in 1974, and then to Manchester City in 1978. They went their own way but were reunited at Barnsley.

Greg Campbell, whose dad Bobby was Chelsea's manager, has had spells with West Ham, Brighton, Plymouth, and Sparta Rotterdam while Paul Redknapp, son of Bournemouth boss Harry, is on Tottenham's books.

In Scotland the McLean brothers are managers - Jim at Dundee United and Tommy at Motherwell.

Hugo Maradona (recognise the surname!) is with Rayo Vallecano in Spain while his better known brother, Diego, achieved world fame in Argentina and Italy.

Maybe one day Roy Race will manage England...and Roy junior will score the winning goal in the World Cup Final.

John Charles (left), Martin (top), Clive (right) and Bradley (above) make up the Allen trio.

MIGHTY MOUSE

BEFORE HE TEAMED-UP WITH HOT-SHOT HAMISH, KEVIN 'MIGHTY' MOUSE WAS A STUDENT AT ST. VICTOR'S HOSPITAL AND A PART-TIME PLAYER FOR TOTTENFORD ROVERS, IN THE FIRST DIVISION. KEVIN WAS ALSO IN CHARGE OF THE ST. VICTOR'S HOSPITAL TEAM AT THE HOSPITAL. HE SHARED A ROOM WITH DENNIS, WHO WORKED IN THE SAME WARD. ONE NIGHT . . .

NEXT DAY, AT TOTTENFORD'S GROUND...
WAKE UP, MOUSIE ...TIME TO GET OUT THERE!
WHAT ARE YOU DREAMING OF, SUNSHINE?
STOP TALKING TO ME ABOUT DREAMS!
MIGHTY MOUSE PLAYED WELL...
MOUSE! MOUSE! MIGHTY MOUSE!
I'M FORGETTING DENNIS... HE'S BARMY, ANYWAY!
TOTTENFORD KEPT UP THEIR ATTACKS...
CORNER!
KEEP UP THE PRESSURE, LADS ...THEY'LL CRACK!
BUT...
OHHHHH!
HARD LUCK, KEVIN!
GOOD SAVE, THAT!
THERE WERE CHANCES GALORE...
I'M NOT GOING TO SCORE! IT'LL BE A NIL-NIL DRAW! SO POTTY OLD DENNIS'S DREAM CAN'T COME TRUE!
THEN...
CHASE IT, MOUSIE... IT'S ALL YOURS!
IT'S A GIFT! I CAN'T MISS THIS ONE!

MOUSE HAS DONE IT! HURRAAAAAY!

BUT KEVIN'S SHOT HAD LOOSENED THE BAR AND...
WATCH IT, MOUSIE!
GNURRRR!

LATER...
WH-WHAT HAPPENED?
WE WON! ONE-NIL! GREAT GOAL OF YOURS, MOUSIE!
YOU WERE CARTED OFF. NO HARM DONE...JUST A BUMP ON THE NUT!
MOUSE WENT BACK TO ST. VICTOR'S...
I SAID YOU'D GET CARTED OFF, DIDN'T I?
OH, BE QUIET ...I DON'T WANT TO KNOW ABOUT YOUR DREAMS!

LATER...
OHHHH! ARRRRGHHH!
HE'S AT IT AGAIN!

MOUSE SHOOK DENNIS AWAKE...
ALL RIGHT, TELL ME! WHAT HAPPENED IN YOUR DREAM?
IT— IT WAS TOMORROW'S MATCH. ST. VICTOR'S AGAINST ST. LUKE'S IN THE HOSPITALS CUP...

YOU SCORE THE WINNING GOAL, KEVIN! A LOVELY HEADER...
OKAY. AND WHAT HAPPENS AFTER?

A MAN RUSHES ON TO THE PITCH. HE'S GOT A STICK!
I DON'T LIKE IT!

I DON'T KNOW WHAT HAPPENED NEXT... YOU WOKE ME!
YOU OUGHT TO BE LOCKED UP! GO BACK TO SLEEP... AND LEAVE ME ALONE!

ST. LUKE'S v. ST. VICTOR'S...
I'VE GOT A LOVELY TREAT ARRANGED FOR YOU LADS... IF YOU WIN THE HOSPITALS CUP. SO GO OUT THERE AND PLAY FOR ME!
OOOH, I LIKE NICE TREATS, DOCTOR MENDER!
I WONDER WHAT IT CAN BE?
HMM... AND I WONDER HOW MANY PEOPLE IN THE CROWD HAVE GOT GREAT, BIG STICKS WITH THEM?

ST. VICTOR'S WERE NOT VERY GOOD...
RUBBISH!
YOU'RE USELESS!
YOU CAN'T EVEN KICK PROPERLY!

MIGHTY MOUSE DEFENDED...
GOOD KICK, MOUSIE. GOOD SAVE, TOO!
YOU'RE SUPPOSED TO DO THE SAVING, OSWALD! WHY DON'T YOU DO A BIT OF WORK ...INSTEAD OF JUST WATCHING?
10

WHEN MIGHTY MOUSE WENT UPFIELD...
THERE'S A CHANCE FOR YOU, NEVILLE! JUST BOOT IT FORWARD!
2
THIS IS WHERE I GET MY NAME IN THE PAPERS!

HAW, HAW! HE MISSED IT!
YOU'LL GET YOUR NAME IN THE PAPERS, ALL RIGHT! IT'S THE BIGGEST MISS OF THE MATCH!

IT WAS NIL-NIL AT HALF-TIME...
YOU'RE DOING ALL RIGHT, LADS. AT LEAST, YOU'RE NOT LOSING. NOW YOU KEEP UPFIELD, KEVIN...AND GET A GOAL! YOU'RE THE ONLY ONE LIKELY TO SHOOT STRAIGHT!
IT'S ALWAYS ME! I HAVE TO DO EVERYTHING!

BUT, TIME PASSED...AND STILL NO SCORE...
AHHHH! HOW ABOUT IT, REF? PENALTY!
NO FOUL. PLAY ON... FAIR ENOUGH SHOULDER-CHARGE!
GET A GOAL, KEVIN. THERE'S ONLY A COUPLE OF MINUTES LEFT!

THE BALL WENT BEHIND FOR A GOAL-KICK...
EVERYONE MOVE UP. I'LL GIVE THIS A REALLY BIG WHACK!
WE'VE HAD IT. WE'LL NEVER SCORE NOW...

OHHHH! WHO DID THAT?
WHOOPS! MY FOOT SLIPPED!

WELL, MY FOOT'S SLIPPED, TOO!

KEVIN'S SHOT WAS SUPER!
LOVELY GOAL, MOUSIE!
THAT'S NOT FAIR... HE KICKED IT AT ME!
IT'S THERE!
GOLLY, I'VE SCORED! WE'RE IN THE LEAD!
AND ST. VICTOR'S WON ...ONE-NIL!
GOOD GAME!
WELL PLAYED!
YOU DID IT! YOU'VE WON US THE HOSPITALS CUP! GREAT GOAL, MOUSE!
DENNIS'S DREAM! THE MAN WITH THE STICK! IT'S DOCTOR MENDER! HE'S GOING TO WHACK ME ONE!
BUT...
YOU WON THE CUP FOR US, KEVIN. YOU LOVELY LITTLE PLAYER!
HOW EMBARRASSING! BUT AT LEAST HE'S NOT USING HIS STICK ON ME!
ST. VICTOR'S ARE PROUD OF YOU, LADS... AND NOW I'LL TELL YOU WHAT YOUR TREAT IS! YOU'RE ALL GOING OFF TO SPEND CHRISTMAS IN THE SUNSHINE... A NICE HOLIDAY FOR YOU! YOU DESERVE IT!
SCHIAFFINO!
HAPPY CHRISTMAS, MOUSIE. SMASHING HERE, ISN'T IT? LIKE A DREAM COME TRUE!
DON'T SAY THINGS LIKE THAT, DENNIS... I'VE HAD ENOUGH OF YOU AND YOUR DREAMS!
I'VE BOOKED A ROOM FOR HIM... ON HIS OWN!
THE END.

DARREN ANDERTON

(Tottenham)

Darren Anderton's sensational performances during Portsmouth's bid for FA Cup Glory and promotion to the new Premier League in 1992 had the big clubs' talent scouts flocking to Fratton Park.

This tricky winger hails from Southampton, Portsmouth's fiercest rivals, and although he played for school representative teams, the Saints allowed him to slip through their fingers.

Darren first came to national attention with two tremendous goals in a fourth round FA Cup tie against Leyton Orient. Middlesbrough were the next to suffer in a fifth round replay as he scored two goals and made two others. Then for good measure he rocked mighty Liverpool with the opening goal in Pompey's semi-final against The Reds at Highbury.

All this made the shy 20-year-old a very hot property indeed, and Spurs won the race for his signature with a £2 million bid in June 1992.

McCLAIR MAGIC!

(1) SUPER-SCOT Brian McClair charges in for the goal that spelled Rumbelows Cup glory for Manchester United against Nottingham Forest. (2) Celebration time as Paul Ince and Mark Hughes share the joy. (3) 'We've done it', match-winner McClair hoists the trophy aloft. (EOP)

IT'S A FUNNY

Goalkeepers not born in this country are playing an increasing role on the domestic scene.

BRUCE GROBBELAAR

One of the most colourful characters in British football, Bruce is a great entertainer!

ENGLISH football has long prided itself on its great goalkeeping traditions, but this hasn't stopped clubs looking to Europe and beyond for top-quality stoppers.

The variety of names - Grobbelaar, Ogrizovic, Schmeichel, Thorstvedt and Miklosko for example - show how wide the net has been cast as our clubs seek perfection in a position in which the Football League has created a rich tradition.

Leading the current crop is Liverpool ace BRUCE GROBBELAAR, who was also 'discovered' in unusual circumstances. Bruce was in Britain on holiday during the 1978-79 season and spent some time playing for Crewe Alexandra. His displays there came to the attention of Liverpool, who snapped him up two years later, paying the Canadian Club Vancouver Whitecaps a £250,000 fee.

Bruce is as much an entertainer as a keeper - his acrobatic style and dashes from goal have made him a favourite around the world. When he won his first League Cup medal at Wembley, he walked on his hands around the hallowed pitch; when Liverpool and Roma were locked in a penalty shoot-out in the European Cup final, Bruce's wobbly-knees act so distracted Italian Graziani that he blazed his kick over the bar; and when a Spanish crowd pelted him with oranges Bruce picked one up and ate it!

OLD NAME!

South African-born, Bruce played international football for his adopted country Zimbabwe and this dashed his hopes of playing for England.

STEVE OGRIZOVIC was once Bruce's understudy at Liverpool - and he had previously played the number two role to Ray Clemence at the club. 'Big Oggy' was born in Mansfield, the son of a Yugoslav miner who had moved to England for work. After Ogrizovic had trained as a police cadet, Arthur Cox signed him for Chesterfield at the start of the 1977-78 season. After just 12 games for Chesterfield, Liverpool paid £70,000 for the promising youngster. Oggy's five years at Anfield saw him make just five first-team appearances, though he picked up two European Cup winners' medals by sitting on the subs' bench at the 1978 and 1981 finals.

After a spell at Shrewsbury, Ogrizovic moved to Coventry in 1984 for £72,000. He has been a fixture in the Sky Blues' side since and starred in their memorable 1987 FA Cup Final win over Tottenham. By that time Oggy was on the fringe of international honours and played as a second half substitute for Bobby Robson's Football League side against the Rest of Europe at Wembley, also in 1987.

Steve's other great love is cricket. As a bowler with minor county side Shropshire, he once clean bowled the great West Indian batsman Viv Richards in a NatWest Trophy tie - only for the umpire to rule the delivery a no-ball'!

PETER SCHMEICHEL achieved his lifelong ambition when Manchester United paid Danish Club Brondy £600,000 for the 6ft 6 in blond star in 1991. As a youngster Peter used to treasure his replica Gary Bailey kit, marketed by the then-United 'keeper. Peter decided to settle in Denmark in 1960 after touring there. He was quickly dubbed 'Peter the Great' after building up an impressive number of clean sheets in his first season at Old Trafford. Schmeichel has followed compatriots Jan Sivebaek and Jesper Olsen to Old Trafford. He says: "Before moving to England I spoke to Jesper and Jan Molby of Liverpool. They told me a lot about English football and

ERIK THORSTVEDT

Spurs' popular Norwegian goalkeeper almost ended up playing for North London rivals Arsenal—he failed to get a work permit!

PETER SCHMEICHEL

Manchester United paid a Danish Club £600,000 for the blond star in 1991. He's proved a bargain!

JAN STEJSKAL

The Czechoslovakian goalkeeper was playing for Sparta Prague until Queens Park Rangers snapped him up. His early days in England were tough and he lost his first team spot for a time.

LUDEK MIKLOSKO

West Ham United were the buyers of Miklosko, who was Stejskal's rival in the Czech national team. He has tasted life in both top divisions.

IT'S A FUNNY OLD NAME!

told me that United were the biggest club of the lot."

ERIK THORSTVEDT, Tottenham's popular Norwegian goalkeeper, could have ended up playing for arch-rivals Arsenal. Eric had trials with the Gunners and QPR as a youngster and Arsenal's bid to lure him from Borussia Moenchengladbach failed only because they were unable to obtain a work permit.

Erik eventually moved to Spurs from IFK Gothenburg in December 1988. That was six years after he first came to White Hart Lane as a hopeful trialist with his home-town club Viking Stavanger. The Norwegian star suffered a nightmare debut in England when, in front of a live TV audience, he let a shot from Nottingham Forest's Nigel Clough slip through his hands and into the net. That earned him the unflattering nickname of 'Erik the Unready'!

But before long his displays elevated him to Spurs' most popular goalkeeper since Pat Jennings. He showed his appreciation to the Spurs fans by throwing his gloves to the fans after each victory - once jumping the gun, when, after throwing away his gloves, Erik discovered that the referee had blown for a free-kick and not full-time!

Thorstvedt's career at Tottenham turned full circle when he won an FA Cup winners medal in 1991 - ironically against Forest, the team that had made his bow into English football such a tough one.

Leading the Czech invasion into the Barclays League are international goalkeeping rivals JAN STEJSKAL of Queens Park Rangers and West Ham's LUDEK MIKLOSKO. Rangers snapped up Stejskal from Sparta Prague following the 1990 World Cup. But like Thorstvedt, Jan found his early days in England tough. Miklosko had a happier time initially following his move from Banik Ostrava, helping West Ham to promotion in 1991. Miklosko was the Czech number one for five years before losing his place to Stejskal.

So there you have it. More foreign players have appeared on the domestic scene. It just so happens that goalkeeper can claim more 'funny' names than other positions.....!

ALAN SHEARER
(Southampton)

This dynamic young centre-forward has become one of the hottest properties in the modern game. Born in Newcastle on 13 August 1970, he first hit the headlines when at the age of 17 years and 240 days he became the youngest scorer of a First Division hat-trick. The fact that he achieved this against a powerful Arsenal side in only his second full match makes his achievement all the more remarkable.

The next time Alan hit the headlines was in the Toulon Under-21 Tournament in May 1991 when he top-scored with 7 goals as England won the Tournament for the second successive year. After a string of impressive performances for Saints, Alan was called-up in February 1992 for his full England debut against France and, almost inevitably, scored in England's 2-0 victory.

With Gary Lineker retiring from international football after the 1992 European Championships, Alan is a prime candidate to be Gary's successor.

CAN YOU MANAGE?

The Home Countries have been enjoying great success lately. How much do you know about the men in charge?

GRAHAM TAYLOR

England

It is a success story based on belief, a determination to be the best, of striving for a target, and reaching it.

In Graham Taylor's case it was to be a relentless pursuit of the top job in football.

And if his skills as a player were not sharp enough to reach the goals he set himself, then Taylor was determined he would become first a good coach, then a great manager.

It meant putting himself into situations where he survived by quickness of thought, and an ability to be dramatically persuasive.

As a young player at Grimsby Town, Taylor knew deep down he wasn't good enough to be a star, but he did discover he could talk, and people would listen.

One of his first jobs after training had finished was to work for one of the Town directors who ran a stall selling seaside novelties.

The young Taylor would wait at the railway station to meet the Yorkshire holiday-makers who, free for two weeks from the drudgery of the coal mines, were ready to spend their money.

Taylor sold bottles of Cleethorpes air. "Best fresh air" he would sing out to the miners and their families. "Come on, buy your jar. Sniff the seaside."

Of course the jars were empty. But Taylor was so persuasive, did such a good job, that he was quickly promoted to the bingo stall.

It was a lesson that was to stay with him for the rest of his young life. Simply you could do anything if you wanted to.

He wanted to be a good player. He was but only good enough to be a regular in the lower divisions of the Football League.

But he loved the game, and loved even more talking about it. Arguing tactics, the pattern of play, and people listened.

He went into management with Lincoln City, and promptly lost his first nine games. That was where his self belief took over.

Protected by a board of directions who were prepared to be patient, Taylor slowly began to get the kind of results he knew he was capable of achieving.

He got his message home in team talks that were both thorough and passionate. Others began to believe in him, too.

Lincoln prospered with promotion and Taylor was soon about to be paid the greatest compliment of his short but successful career.

Unstoppable

Pop star Elton John, then the supremo of Third Division Watford, wanted a new manager for his ambitious club. The short list was narrowed down to two names...Bobby Moore, England's World Cup winning captain and a legend in the game and Graham Taylor. Taylor got the job.

From then on he became unstoppable, and Watford moved through to the First Division, an F.A. Cup Final, and a heady season of European adventure.

Taylor had arrived, and already he was being mentioned as a man who may one day go all the way to Lancaster Gate.

He was a manager who was a winner. Who could buy, and sell, produce exciting teams, was sound tactically, and for good measure, could project himself brilliantly.

To the media he was a Godsend. He could defend his style of football, talk for minutes about his players, why Watford won, and why they lost.

It was no surprise that he moved to Aston Villa, and quickly restored them back to the First Division.

It was inevitable that once Bobby Robson's days were numbered as England manager Taylor would once again go on a short list...this time for the biggest job of all.

There were contenders such as Terry Venables of Tottenham, Howard Kendall of Everton, Steve Coppell of Crystal Palace, and inevitably Brian Clough of Nottingham Forest.

Once again Taylor won the poll, got the job he had dreamed about when selling 5p jars of Cleethorpes air.

He's still talking nineteen to the dozen. Rarely finishing a sentence before seizing on something else to say.

And that's the appeal of the man. He'll give you his time, precious though it may be to him.

Away from his beloved football, he is a Buddy Holly fan, enjoys the theatre, where he admits he can escape from the pressures of being a winner.

He wants that more than anything, and believes how he does with England, will be how he is judged by the Nation.

His ambition is simple. To win the World Cup. Only then will he stop striving, stop trying to be the best.

JACK CHARLTON

Republic of Ireland

Big Jack, now officially an honorary Irishman after taking the Republic to the quarter finals of the World Cup in 1990, has the unique distinction of being as successful in management as he was as a player.

Jack O'Charlton as they call him in the bars of Dublin, where over a pint of Guinness they talk fondly of the Englishman who gave a brand new identity to a Nation. A rebel who found a cause.

As a player with Leeds United, Charlton was the cornerstone of Don Revie's great side that dominated English football in the late sixties and early seventies.

And as Sir Alf Ramsey's centre half, he was the towering influence in the England side who, in 1966, became World Champions at Wembley.

"He was always the player who most questioned my tactics and decisions," remembers Ramsey. "Jack always wanted to know

ANDY ROXBURGH

Scotland

Andy Roxburgh is the quiet man of Scottish football. A manager who like Graham Taylor enjoyed little success as a player.

As a workaday mid-fielder, Roxburgh achieved little in spells with Partick Thistle and Falkirk, and it was not until he moved into coaching that he bagan to show his true talents.

And now, Roxburgh must follow a proud Scottish heritage. They have played in the last five World Cup Finals. Andy must make it six, or perish.

Such is the desire for Scotland to be great again, that nothing but the best is demanded for the team.

Supporters believe they are blood brothers to the Brazilians, linked by an arrogant belief in skill technique and talent.

Like the men before him, Roxburgh knows he must get his country to the USA in 1994.

In 1974, Willie Ormond took them to Germany, in 78 it was Ally McCloud and Argentina, in 82 Jock Stein, and four years later Alex Ferguson in Mexico.

why I was doing this, or changing that."

Dominating in the air, Charlton gave England and Leeds height in the penalty area. And Revie regularly used him at set pieces where he would station himself alongside the opposing goalkeeper to compete for free-kicks and corners.

It was his hard, uncompromising attitude that impressed Revie and Ramsey. Always in the shadow of his more famous younger brother, Bobby, Jack always had to scrap for his recognition.

That bred in him a fierce desire to do well, to be an achiever.

He showed that same ruthless desire when he stepped into management, first taking Middlesbrough from the Second Division to the First, then walking out on Newcastle when supporters began to question his methods.

Charlton would never sit back and accept unjustified criticism, he was too much his own man to take it.

And that same deep belief in his ability to get a job done transformed the Republic of Ireland when he became their manager six years ago.

His re-building of a team who produced gifted players but never the same degree of performance, was not without controversy.

Again Charlton had his critics. He laughed in their faces as he constructed a team who became one of the most feared in the World.

It was built on long ball football. Players who could get the ball forward quickly, and others able to join quickly in their support of it.

"I agree, it's not pretty," admitted Charlton."But it's pretty effective."

Under him, the Republic flourished as never before. He produced a team who prospered from their long ball football, and plundered their way to successes in the European Championships of 1988, and the World Cup two years later.

All Charlton did, was make it very hard for teams to play against the Irish.

Now Jack looks forward to the World Cup, after the disappointment of not making it to Sweden.

That's Charlton. What you see is what you can get. An honest man, a dedicated manager. Only time will tell if he will receive the credit he deserves.

All four men had proved themselves in club management. All four had been tried and tested. Roxburgh is the exception.

He first made his name by taking a talented youth side to a tournament in Mexico and producing performances of class and quality.

That was ten years ago, and now the quiet man is looking for success again.

He was brought in six years ago to succeed Ferguson, and is slowly building a side with little bricks and mortar.

But that has always been his trademark. A manager able to pick teams to play to a certain pattern.

Roxburgh is well served by a friendliness which disarms his critics. He is a man who does his best, with raw materials that could be better.

But always he is approachable, affable and that instinct for self preservation to the army of critics who lie in wait for him, has seen him survive a hot seat warmed by a Nation's hunger for success.

The Scots produce brilliant players, but very few great teams. The quiet man knows that, but believes his teams are more durable than those built on blinding skills.

Roxburgh is a team maker, a thorough, methodical man who will do it his way. The price of success is glory...or the guillotine.

TERRY YORATH

Wales

Terry Yorath is the man in pursuit of a dream. And that is simply to lead Wales to qualify for the finals of the World Cup, for the first time since 1958. Nothing more. Nothing less.

Since Sweden 34 years ago, Welsh football has never been represented in the finals of the European Championships, and the World Cup.

It is an ambition that fuels Yorath with the fire and fervour of the Welsh dragon. To succeed on the world stage is all he craves for.

Now it has become a preoccupation. A target, almost a Holy Grail.

The principality has produced so many individual stars, but never a team to gloriously advertise the exploits of a Nation more famous for its rugby than its football.

Wales have failed so many times that it has needed someone like Yorath to shape and mould its destiny.

Here is a man who has been used to success, who won a reputation for sorting teams out, and for setting the right example.

He learned his trade, like Jack Charlton at Leeds, under the awe inspiring Don Revie.

Never quite good enough to

become an automatic first team choice, Yorath was in the United shadow squad. That meant being a faithful reserve to the likes of Norman Hunter, a man in his day only second to the great Bobby Moore.

When he did get into the Leeds team, Yorath made a massive impact. He wore his heart on his sleeve, was a leader.

He loved a challenge, relished a fight. And to play first team football at Elland Road meant scrapping for the right.

Inevitably he would never be content with a role that meant he was always waiting in the wings.

Revie spoke in glowing terms of him, but could never guarantee that coveted first team place.

But others had noticed the contribution that Yorath made, the qualities of leadership, the style, and the battle-hardened attitude of being the best.

Both Tottenham and Coventry utilised those talents, Spurs to such an extent that he became a major influence in the side, a man who on the field was a leader, and who off it, was an ambassador.

It was obvious that management would suit Yorath, that he could channel the ideas, the enthusiasm, and the expert leadership into the productive assets suited to running a club.

Wales turned to him in a desperate effort to harness their individual talent into the kind of team that could make its mark in world football.

But, over the last two years, there has been a change. The best players don't necessarily produce the best team. There must be ruthless pruning of the talent tree.

Yorath has not been afraid to drop star names. But the Welsh don't have enough to be choosey.

There is real hope that Yorath has produced a side that can at last make Welsh hopes come true.

They were so close to qualifying for the European Championships. Only World champions Germany stood in their way.

Management is about passion, about leadership and self belief. Yorath has those talents in abundance. Wales, and its football future, is safe in his hands.

BILLY BINGHAM

N. Ireland

Billy Bingham has lived on his wits so well that he is the longest serving manager of the four Home nations.

A new contract will take him up to the 1994 World Cup, and see him complete 14 years in one of the most difficult jobs in football.

A good tactician, talented enough to work for the international governing body of the game, FIFA, Bingham's association with the Northern Irish is only on a part-time basis.

He has enjoyed the highs of international management, and the lows, the pinnacle being in 1982 and 86, when he lead Northern Ireland to the World Cup Finals, in Spain, and Mexico.

As a player Bingham was a marvellously gifted wingman, with searing pace, who starred for Sunderland, Luton, Everton and Port Vale.

He became an automatic choice for his country, and a footballing favourite with the fans.

Bingham's open friendliness, and his easy going attitude was later to become important ingredients of his success as a manager.

He went on to boss Everton, stepping into the demanding theatre of Goodison Park, seeking to haul the club back into the big time.

It never worked out for him there, or at Mansfield where he also managed for a spell.

Bingham's successes were all to be with Northern Ireland, as he fashioned a team that became famous.

The Irish had in the mid sixties and early seventies perhaps the greatest player Britain has seen.

His name was George Best of Manchester United who was the complete footballer.

But for all his tremendous talent Best could never achieve his own lifetime ambition, to play in the Finals of the European Championship, or World Cup.

Bingham went on to produce teams with lesser talented individuals, but fired with a sense of purpose and national pride.

In 1982 they made it to Spain and beat the host nation in one of the great World Cup upsets.

In 1986, they were back again, qualifying by holding England at Wembley and celebrating for a joyous 48 hours.

Bingham still turns out teams rich in ability, but short of goal scoring power.

He says: "I love the job, and if we could score more goals, we'd be a danger to any side."

But Billy soldiers on with a sparkle in his eye.

Billy enjoys the challenge, loves his football, and craves for more success. And he's optimistic enough to believe he'll get it.

RYAN GIGGS

(Manchester United)

Ryan is the latest teenage sensation to emerge from Old Trafford. So meteoric has been his rise that people are calling him "the Second George Best".

In October 1991 Ryan became the youngest-ever Welsh International at the age of 17 years and 321 days when appearing as a substitute against Germany in Nuremberg for Wales' European Championship qualification crunch match which they lost. All this after being captain of England Schoolboys!

Cardiff-born Ryan qualified for England on a residential basis but is proud to wear the red shirt of Wales. With his electrifying pace, two good feet and a cannonball shot, this young man is destined to go to the very top.

GLO-BALL REPORT...

DATE: 2092

One hundred years from now, the world of football may look a lot different from the game we know today. ROY OF THE ROVERS in the 21st Century may be reporting on news items such as these...

WOMEN'S WORLD CUP

JAN 2092

Carmel Race, older sister of Royce, captained Great Britain ladies to victory over the maidens from Mandelaland (formerly South Africa) in the Women's World Cup Final in Hong Kong. The Lionesses mauled the Gazelles 5-0.

EUROPEAN CHAMPIONSHIP

JUNE 2092

Defending champions Great Britain beat Iberia (formerly Spain and Portugal) in the final, at the 200,000 seater "Race Mega-Stadium" in Melchester.

Britain's star in the tournament was seventeen-year-old Royce Race (great-great-great grandson of the legendary Roy Race) whose nine goals made him top scorer in the competition, taking his total for Great Britain to fifteen, in only two seasons. This puts young Royce on target to overtake (his great-grandfather and former national manager) Royston Race's national record of seventy-five goals in his one hundred and twenty-game career for England & Great Britain, from 2018-2036.

Royce has attracted a number of lucrative transfer offers from overseas clubs, most notably a quarter of a billion pluton bid from an unidentified Far Eastern source.

WORLD CUP

JAN 2094

In the qualifying rounds for the 2094 World Cup Finals, Great Britain have been drawn against the Middle East, Central Russia, the Western United States, and Oceania. The British team are co-favourites to repeat their World success in 2070 and 2082, along with defending world champions - North-East China.

WORLD LEAGUE of SOCCER

In the tenth year of the World League of Soccer, the North London Aces (formerly Tottenham Hotspur, Arsenal and Barnet) lift the world trophy, having beaten the California Cruisers in the last game - thanks to a hat-trick by Geoff Lineker.

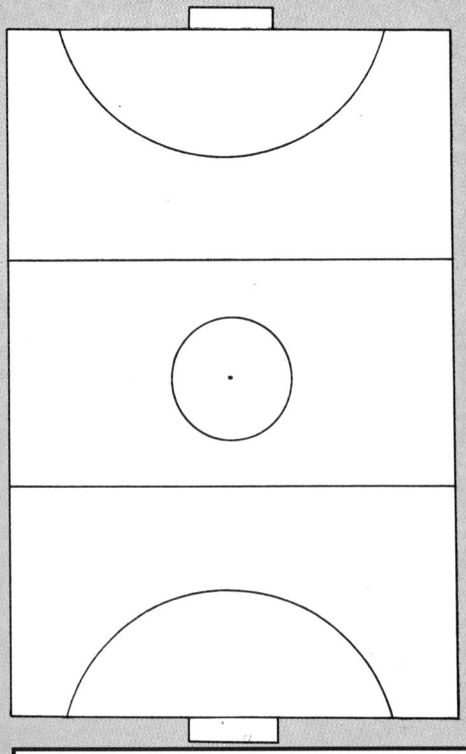

The eleven team World League table finished...

	P	W	D	L	F	A	3g	Pts
NORTH LONDON ACES	20	12	5	3	63	9	6	59
ROMAN RAIDERS	20	12	4	4	59	15	5	57
MELCHESTER ROVERS	20	11	5	4	53	16	6	55
NAIROBI RHINOS	20	8	8	4	48	24	4	44
CALIFORNIA CRUISERS	20	6	8	6	40	31	2	34
MOSCOW MACHINE	20	6	6	8	36	37	3	33
BRASILIA FOREST	20	6	6	8	32	37	2	32
MEXICO CITY SAINTS	20	5	5	10	17	59	1	26
CAPE TOWN CRUSH	20	4	8	8	25	47	1	25
BERLIN BULLS	20	5	4	11	15	63	0	24
TOKYO BULLETS	20	3	5	12	12	62	1	18

*4 points for a win
1 point for a draw
1 point for a win by three or more clear goals(3g)

RULE CHANGES

The pitch is divided into thirds and the game into quarters of an hour, with the clock stopping when the ball goes out of play.

A ball cannot be kicked across the middle third - without being touched by a player.

Players can only be offside in the opposition's third of the field.

Any foul by a defensive player in his own third results in an automatic five minutes in the "sin-bin".

Penalty areas are now rounded with a radius of 20 metres.

Short corners are taken from the intersection of the penalty area and the goal-line.

Teams can only have a maximum of nine players in their defensive third.

THE FUTURE...

2093 sees the promotion of the three teams - Hong Kong Heat, Arabian Knights and South Pole Bears (whose home will be the temperature-controlled Ice Pavilion - five miles north of the South Pole!)

Next season, will herald the first ever Moon Shield - played under the Tranquility Dome on the moon's surface. The North London Aces (World League champions) will face Melchester Rovers (World League Cup champions) in this historic heavenly match-up. This game will pave the way for the introduction to the World League of the Lunar City Rockets, in 2095 - just twenty years after the initial colonisation of the moon's surface.

LEE CHAPMAN
(Leeds United)

Much-travelled Lee Chapman has been one of the most consistent and underrated goalscorers over the past decade. In turn Lincoln-born Lee has played for: Stoke City, Arsenal, Sunderland, Sheffield Wednesday, Niort (France), Nottingham Forest and Leeds United.

Lee was re-united with his old Wednesday boss Howard Wilkinson when Leeds needed extra goal power in 1990 to secure promotion to the First Division.

Lee duly obliged and was the First Division's top scorer in 1990/91 with 31 League and Cup goals in Leeds' successful first campaign back in the top flight. The following season Lee continued in the same vein as Leeds battled with Manchester United for the Championship.

MANCHESTER

DENIS LAW – *WORLD CLASS!*

Arguably, the greatest club in the world. This is their life!

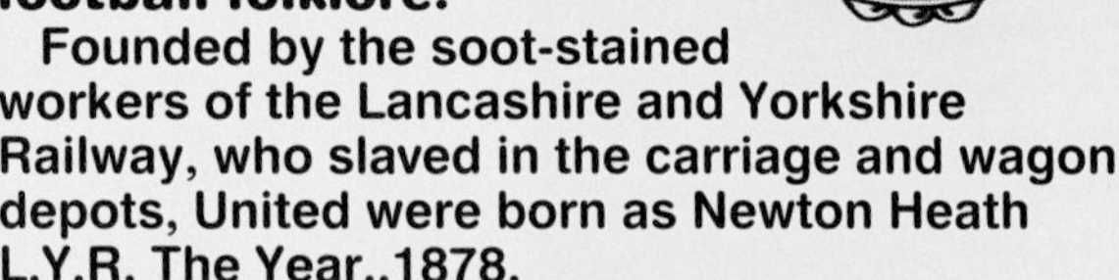

The story of Manchester United is written in grime and glory, built on pride and passion, and forged in the blood red shirts of a dynasty that has become a part of football folklore.

Founded by the soot-stained workers of the Lancashire and Yorkshire Railway, who slaved in the carriage and wagon depots, United were born as Newton Heath L.Y.R. The Year..1878.

Their changing rooms for games was the local public house, and the Heathens as they were known were kept alive by a love and passion for the game that saw them dip into their own pay packets for the right to play.

Tough and highly skilled, they joined the Football League in 1892, and paid six shillings (30 pence) a week for the rent of a cottage that served as their first headquarters.

HARD TIMES

In those days the Heathens played in jerseys of green and gold, and the hint of bankruptcy was never far away.

The club found themselves £1,000 in debt, and heading rapidly for the knackers yard when a former player's dog inadvertently not only helped rescue the Heathens, but helped in the formation of Manchester United.

Ex-striker Harry Stafford who loved the club, organised a four day, fund raising bazaar to save the Heathens.

His dog, a large and friendly St Bernard wandered out of the hall and into a nearby pub owned by businessman J.H. Davies.

The landlord fussed the dog and fed it, before handing it over to his boss. Stafford found out about it, and went to claim his pet.

While with Davies, Stafford poured his heart out about the plight of Newton Heath. The businessman listened with interest.

Eventually, later in 1902, Davies and his

UNITED...

the rise from rags to riches!

group of backers told Stafford they would pay off the Heathens' debts, then around £2,000, by today's standards £2 million.

Forty-one days later after negotiations were completed, the money owed was paid off, and a new club was formed.

Some wanted it called Manchester Central, others Manchester Celtic, but in the end it was decided it should be....Manchester United.

A year later Ernest Mangnall came to the club, and effectively became its first manager.

Success was a foregone conclusion, and Mangnall built a wonder team. Promotion came in 1906, and three years later the first ever Championship when they beat City and Aston Villa, by nine points.

In 1909 the club won their first F.A. Cup Final, beating Bristol City 1-0 at Crystal Palace.

The following year a new stadium costing £60,000 was built close to the dockland area of Salford. It was on the Stretford side of the

BUSBY – *THE LEGEND!*

Manchester Ship Canal in an area known as Old Trafford.

The First World War disrupted life throughout Europe, and by 1922 the club was involved in yet another financial crisis.

They pulled through, setting in motion a series of switchback rides, relegation, promotion yet again, until the outbreak of the Second World War.

LEGENDS BORN

But the pre-war years were soon forgotten as United rose again with a pride in itself and a passion from the people that was infectious and incurable.

It was as if the city itself used the club to symbolise its own soaring, teeming growth. Legends were about to be born.

One of the first was Sir Matt Busby, the Scot

who played for Liverpool and Manchester City before taking over as manager of United.

The war was over. Britain and the rest of Europe were rebuilding, and United were shaping plans for the future too.

They won the F.A. Cup in 1948, but Busby was not satisfied, he knew he had to rebuild the club. Four years later, with the backbone of the side that won so thrillingly at Wembley, they became First Division champions again.

And so the Busby Babes were born, a creation of youthful genius that was to take football by storm, and create another legend.

They were a collection of exciting, brilliant, devastating kids who drew massive crowds to Old Trafford.

As one by one they were introduced to the first team, so each took the stage like a star performer appearing before an adoring audience.

Billy Whelan, Eddie Colman, Mark Jones, Jackie Blanchflower, Bill Foulkes, Geoff Bent, and the greatest of them all, Duncan Edwards.

Other young players like Dennis Viollet were joined by record signings such as Tommy Taylor, the Barnsley centre forward, and United's goalscoring machine was built.

In 1956, the team had bedded down so brilliantly that another Championship was won. And it was so outstanding none other could get near it.

By far the most brilliant player was Edwards, who made his League debut at 16, and who played for England when he was only 18 and 183 days old, the youngest man, for he was a man, to pull on the white shirt of his country.

Edwards was a player so admired by those who saw him or played against him, that he will forever be held in awe.

To show that the 1956 title was no fluke, United won it again in 1957, this time by eight points.

They reached the Cup Final and seemed certain to win the double, but a tragic injury to goalkeeper Ray Wood saw them lose 2-1 to Aston Villa.

They were to return the following year, and be beaten again, but under such circumstances, that football would never forget.

By now, United had become the first English club to play in the newly created European Cup.

In the first adventure into Europe, United gloriously reached the semi-finals, losing to the great Real Madrid of Spain 5-3 on aggregate.

A year later, in search of the success that Busby felt was United's destiny, a team died in the snow and sorrow of Munich airport.

The date was 6th February 1958. United had just drawn with Red Star of Belgrade to reach the semi-finals of the competition yet again.

On the journey home from Yugoslavia, their aircraft landed at Munich to re-fuel. And it was

GEORGE BEST and BOBBY CHARLTON may be spectators now but just ask your Dad what they'd be worth at today's prices?

while attempting to take off in snow and ice for the third time, that the plane crashed.

Roger Bryne, Geoff Bent, Eddie Colman, Mark Jones, David Pegg, Tommy Taylor and Billy Whelan died. Duncan Edwards lived through the crash but died later in hospital.

Johnny Berry and Jackie Blanchflower were never to play football again. Others detained in hospital included the young Bobby Charlton who was just starting a career in football.

Bill Foulkes and Harry Gregg had bravely tried to rescue their colleagues from the wreckage.

Ken Morgan, Albert Scanlon, Dennis Viollet, and Ray Wood were all injured.

The Busby Babes were no more, and Busby himself was fighting for his life in a German hospital. It was a day edged in black for football. One the game would never forget.

So the Championship side of 56 and 57 had been destroyed. Only three of the eleven regular members of the line up would play for the club again.

For weeks Busby lay in hospital and as he slowly began to recover, he also began to realise the horror he had lived through.

"It was impossible to imagine the loss I had experienced," he said. "I felt I could not carry on, but my wife Jean convinced me that the boys who had died would have wanted me to go on. It was hard, but I did it."

United lost to Bolton in an emotional Cup Final that year with a team newly bought and drafted in.

But Busby had begun to rebuild, Bobby Charlton became its new star, and Denis Law a magical and flamboyant acquisition, the fans' favourite with his rapier skills and blinding goals.

In 1963 United won the F.A. Cup, and Law scored one of the goals in the 3-1 victory over Leicester City.

But as the city was settling down again after a week long celebration to honour Busby and his team, a 17-year-old Irish boy was signing professional forms.

He was soon to be the new sensation. Perhaps the greatest player these Islands have produced. His name was George Best.

MUNICH '58

The team that died in the snow and sorrow of Munich Airport. Survivors Dennis Viollet (right) and Albert Scanlon (left) with wives.

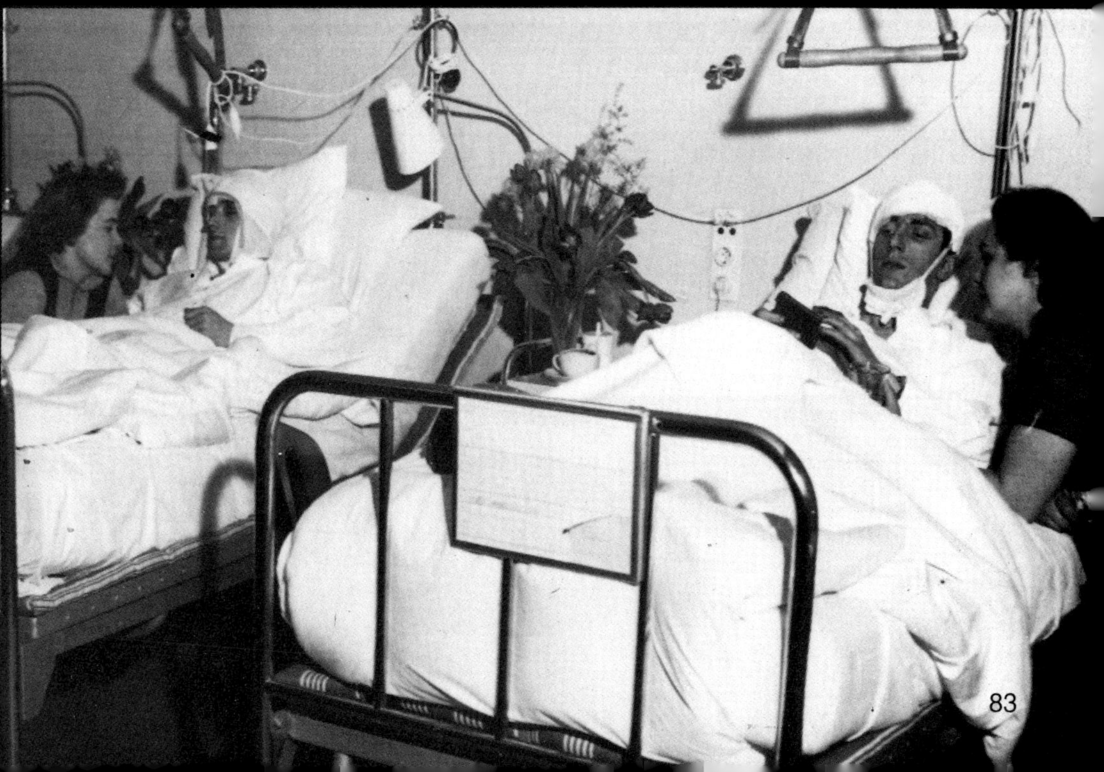

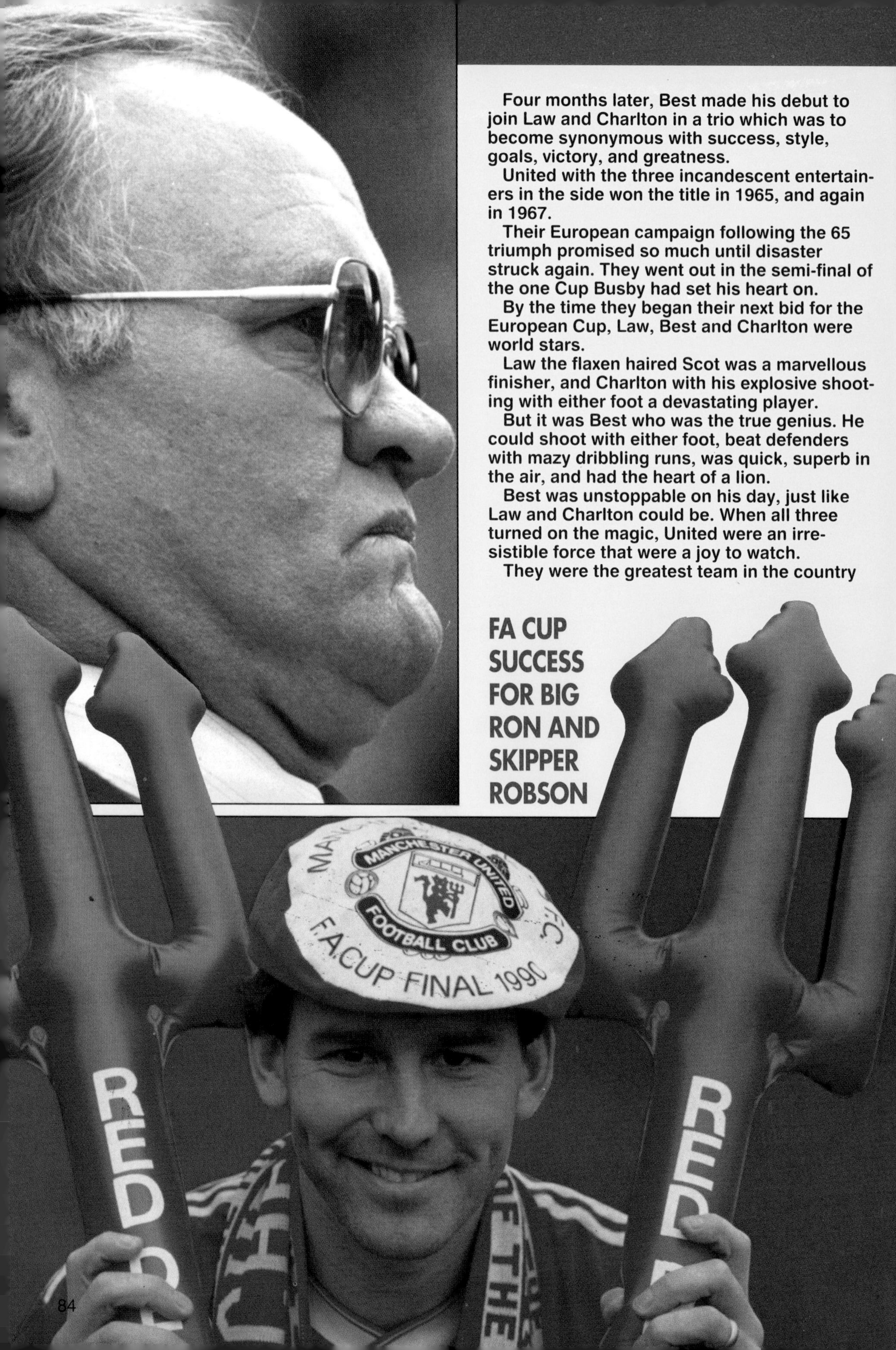

Four months later, Best made his debut to join Law and Charlton in a trio which was to become synonymous with success, style, goals, victory, and greatness.

United with the three incandescent entertainers in the side won the title in 1965, and again in 1967.

Their European campaign following the 65 triumph promised so much until disaster struck again. They went out in the semi-final of the one Cup Busby had set his heart on.

By the time they began their next bid for the European Cup, Law, Best and Charlton were world stars.

Law the flaxen haired Scot was a marvellous finisher, and Charlton with his explosive shooting with either foot a devastating player.

But it was Best who was the true genius. He could shoot with either foot, beat defenders with mazy dribbling runs, was quick, superb in the air, and had the heart of a lion.

Best was unstoppable on his day, just like Law and Charlton could be. When all three turned on the magic, United were an irresistible force that were a joy to watch.

They were the greatest team in the country

FA CUP SUCCESS FOR BIG RON AND SKIPPER ROBSON

again. Inventive, full of flair, entertainers, winners, joyous believers in wonderful cretion.

So destiny saw United face Benfica at Wembley Stadium on the 29th May, 1968, ten years after Munich.

No United fan will forget the date for so much of the club's history was wrapped into one game.

Bobby Charlton scored first, Benfica equalised to take the Final into extra time.

United had no Law in their side. He was injured. But they had Best, and they had Charlton.

And it was Best who scored a marvellous goal to put United 2-1 ahead, and after Brian Kidd had got the third, Charlton sealed victory with his second.

There were many tears spilled that night. From fans, players and from Busby himself. United were the first English side to win the European Cup.

Surely now United would stride on to even greater glories. Sadly it was not to be.

The team that had made an old man proud began to disintegrate around the grandeur of Old Trafford.

The final, killing blow came at the end of the 1964 season when United, European champions six years earlier, were relegated to the Second Division.

Tommy Docherty, by now manager after taking over from Frank O'Farrell, promised United would be back. He was true to his word.

The following season, the Reds were champions of the Second Division, the good times beckoned once more.

In 1976 United reached Wembley again, but lost the Cup Final 1-0 to Southampton.

But the old fires were burning again, stoked by the irrepressible Docherty, and in 1977 they returned to the famous old stadium.

This time they beat Liverpool 2-1 to deny them the treble. Two years later, 1979, they were at Wembley yet again with Dave Sexton now manager in place of Docherty.

There was to be no happy ending this time. 2-0 ahead, they lost 3-2 to Arsenal, the winning goal coming in the last minute. Sexton was later sacked.

Ron Atkinson came in as manager and brought with him Bryan Robson as his skipper and midfield influence.

United won at Wembley in 1983 beating Brighton 4-0 in a replay, after drawing 2-2. That season they beat Liverpool to win the Charity Shield.

Two years later they won the Cup again, beating Everton 1-0, and after losing defender Kevin Moran, sent off in the second half.

After Atkinson had gone, a victim of United's inability to bring another Championship back to Old Trafford, it was Alex Ferguson who was given the task of restoring the glory days in the League.

He led them to yet another F.A. Cup Final triumph in 1990, beating Crystal Palace 1-0 again in a replay after drawing 3-3.

So skipper Robson had lifted the Cup for the third time, and Ferguson began slowly but surely building a team that could achieve the next ambition. The League title.

It is a quest the Scot believes is his own Holy Grail. An ambition that a City needs, for the deeds of its football club, represent the very heartbeat of its people.

United march on. What further triumphs lie ahead?

FERGIE'S LAST LAUGH?

SUPER SCOTS!

ALLY Mc COIST (Rangers.)

Record goal scorer for the club. One of the great strikers in Scottish football. Promises goals and always produces.

SUPER SCOTS!

ANDY GORAM (Rangers.)

Goalkeeper who has come into the side under Walter Smith and shown himself to be a big hit with the club. Capable, safe with good hands, learned his basics in the Football League, and is now rated Scotland's best.

SUPER SCOTS!

PAUL McSTAY (Celtic)

One of the great midfield players not only in Scotland, but European football. Wonderfully gifted and artistic. Gets forward to claim vital goals.

GARY'S GOLDEN BOOTS

GREAT GAME, LADS! THE BEST RUN WE'VE HAD IN THE CUP FOR YEARS!
IT SURE IS... BECAUSE GARY CAN'T STOP SCORING!
WEMBLEY, HERE WE COME!
THEN...
ENOUGH OF THE CHATTER! I'VE GOT SOME EXCITING NEWS! AVONDALE WANDERERS HAVE STOLEN A MARCH ON THE REST OF THE FOOTBALL LEAGUE!
WHY? WHAT HAVE WE DONE?
WE HAVE BEEN INVITED TO REPRESENT THIS COUNTRY IN A FRIENDLY MATCH IN MOSCOW... IN AID OF RUSSIAN CHILDREN'S CHARITIES!
SOCCER IS SOCCER, NO MATTER WHERE YOU PLAY!
TELL YOU WHAT, GARY... IF YOU SCORE A GOAL IN THAT RUSSIAN GAME, I'LL BUY YOU THE MOST EXPENSIVE PAIR OF BOOTS YOU CAN FIND... TO REPLACE THAT TATTY OLD PAIR!
OKAY, GEORGE– YOU'RE ON!
AND WHEN AVONDALE REACHED MOSCOW, THEY HAD ALSO REACHED THE F.A. CUP FINAL...
NOW LISTEN, LADS... I KNOW THIS IS A BIG PRESTIGE MATCH, BUT IT'S ONLY A FRIENDLY! REMEMBER WEMBLEY...
DON'T WORRY, BOSS... WE WON'T GET INJURED!
WE'LL TAKE IT EASY!
GOOAALL!
GARY'S SCORED! ANOTHER OF HIS FIRST-MINUTE JOBS!

AND THE YOUNG STRIKER FOLLOWED IT UP WITH TWO MORE!

GOOAALL! A REAL BLOCKBUSTER!

GOOAALL! A SCREAMER!

YOU DID IT, GARY... A HAT-TRICK! WHEN WE GET BACK, I'LL BUY YOU THE BEST PAIR OF BOOTS ON THE MARKET!

MOSKVA

...AS LONG AS YOU THROW THOSE OLD ONES AWAY! THEY'RE A DISGRACE! JUST LOOK AT 'EM... FALLING TO PIECES...!

MY OLD BOOTS! MAYBE GEORGE IS RIGHT... I'M A GOALSCORER, NO MATTER **WHAT** BOOTS I WEAR! BUT I CAN'T JUST **THROW** THEM AWAY...

BUT THE NEW BOOTS DID NOT SCORE GOALS!
WHAT A MISS!
GARY GRANT WAS IN THE SIX-YARD BOX, TOO! A REAL SITTER!
HE ALWAYS PUTS THOSE AWAY!
WHAT'S HAPPENED TO HIM, BOSS? HE HASN'T SCORED IN FOUR GAMES!
BEATS ME. EVERY STRIKER GOES THROUGH IT AT SOME TIME. IT'S A LEAN SPELL!
I CAN'T DO A THING RIGHT IN FRONT OF GOAL... AND IT ALL STARTED WITH THESE EXPENSIVE NEW BOOTS!
IF I'M NOT CAREFUL, I WON'T BE IN THE TEAM FOR WEMBLEY. I'VE GOT TO GET MY OLD BOOTS BACK, COME WHAT MAY!
RUSSIAN EMBASSY
VERY WELL, COMRADE. I WILL CONTACT THE SON OF THE PRESIDENT AND PUT YOUR OLD BOOTS ON A PLANE AS SOON AS POSSIBLE!
ER... THANK YOU... ER... COMRADE!
ON FRIDAY EVENING...
SORRY, GARY. YOU'RE ON THE BENCH TOMORROW. IT'S YOUR LEAN SPELL...
I UNDERSTAND, BOSS. I'VE NOT BEEN SCORING THE GOALS...

NIET. NOT A BOMB.
PACKAGE FOR WEMBLEY STADIUM- URGENT!
THE SOCCER SHOWPIECE OF THE YEAR... AND AVONDALE WERE IN TERRIBLE TROUBLE!
3-0 AND ONLY FIFTEEN MINUTES TO GO! THEY'VE DESTROYED US!
AFTER COMING ALL THE WAY TO WEMBLEY, WHAT A DISAPPOINTMENT!
AND THEN...
SPECIAL DELIVERY FOR MR GARY GRANT!
MY OLD BOOTS! IT MUST BE!
GET 'EM ON, GARY- AND GET OUT ON THE PARK! YOU'VE GOT A GOAL-SCORING JOB TO DO LIKE YOU'VE NEVER HAD BEFORE!
OKAY, BOSS!
I FEEL A DIFFERENT PLAYER ALREADY! THIS IS OUR BIG CHANCE, BOOTS, LET'S TAKE 'EM APART!
LEFT FOOT!
GOOAALL!

RIGHT FOOT!
GOOAALL!
LEFT FOOT!
GOOAALL!
RIGHT FOOT!
GOOAALL!
FOUR GOALS IN TEN MINUTES! FANTASTIC!
GARY GRANT IS MAGIC!
HE MAKES ROY OF THE ROVERS LOOK LIKE A LEARNER!
4-3! AVONDALE HAVE WON THE CUP!
A SENSATIONAL FINISH!
BUT IN HIS MOMENT OF TRIUMPH, GARY DIDN'T FORGET!
THANK YOU, OLD BOOTS! YOU MADE IT ALL POSSIBLE. I'LL GET YOU REPAIRED— AND I'LL NEVER GET RID OF YOU AGAIN!
The End